Treat The Earth Gently

An Environmental Resource Guide

By Sherrill B. Flora

Cover Design by Margaretia De Paulis

Inside Illustrations by Wendy Meath-Nelson

*The pages of this book
were printed on recycled paper with
a vegetable-based ink: Agri-Ink*

Publishers
T.S. Denison and Company, Inc.
Minneapolis, Minnesota 55431

T.S. DENISON & CO., INC.

DEDICATION

To my husband "G," who always encourages, supports and respects everything that I do and who has always believed in treating the earth gently!

Standard Book Number: 513-02049-7
Treat The Earth Gently
Copyright © 1991 by the T.S. Denison & Co., Inc.
Minneapolis, Minnesota 55431

CONTENTS

Unit 1
ACID RAIN

CONTENTS

Acid Rain Is Invisible!
What Is It Doing To Our Environment?

IMAGINE THE EARTH'S FORESTS
(an activity to be read to the students)

Acid rain is a term that many of you have probably heard on the television news, read about in the newspaper, or heard people discussing. The concept of what "acid rain" is can be very difficult to understand because we cannot see it. Even though we cannot see acid rain, we can easily see the damage that it is doing to our environment. Acid rain results when rainwater in the clouds mixes with harmful substances that have been released into the atmosphere.

Before we begin our study of acid rain, lets take a few minutes and think about the earth and it's beautiful forests. Close your eyes and imagine tall, strong, green trees swaying in the breeze. Think about the lakes filled with crystal blue water and inhabited with many leaping healthy fish. In the forests you can see a wide variety of animals, busy making their homes, searching for all sorts of good food to eat and having an abundance of good clean water to drink. Overhead, the blue skies are filled with soaring birds singing as they fly and then swoop down to pearch in the trees. It's a beautiful picture isn't it!

(Take a few minutes to discuss this imagery with your students.
What comments do the students have to add to this picture?)

Now, let's try to imagine our earth and it's forests again. Are you ready? Close your eyes. This time as you are thinking about our forests the picture will be different. You will hear about some of the things that acid rain is doing to our forests. The trees are no longer tall, strong or green. They are not growing as healthy as they once did. The green leaves are fading and the great pine trees are losing their pine needles. All this is happening because the soil is polluted. The water in the lakes is polluted. The fish are dying and the forest animals do not have enough clean water to drink. The birds that once filled the skies have left to search for clean water or have died because of drinking polluted water! This is not such a pretty picture!

(Take time to discuss with your students how they felt when you read the above
paragraph. Did it make them sad? Which description of the earth's forests
did they like best?)

DRAW A COMPARISON PICTURE
Have each of your students draw a comparison picture. Using a large sheet of white construction paper, have the children fold the paper in half. On one side the children should draw a picture of the earth's forest from the first paragraph you read. On the other half of the paper, the children should draw a picture of what acid rain can do to the earth's forests.

BRAINSTORMING!

Make a list of all the "living things" that you can see in a forest.
Remember that plants are living things too!
Use the back of this paper or another sheet of paper if you need to.

_____   _____

_____   _____

_____   _____

_____   _____

_____   _____

_____   _____

_____   _____

_____   _____

_____   _____

_____   _____

_____   _____

_____   _____

This is an excellent cooperative learning activity. Divide the children into groups of 4 to 6 and let them "brainstorm" together.

Where Does Acid Rain Come From?

Now that you understand some of the things that "acid rain" can do to the environment, lets try to understand what **"ACID RAIN"** is and where it comes from.

Acid rain results from burning **COAL, OIL** and **NATURAL GAS.**
Coal, oil and natural gas are called **FOSSIL FUELS** because they were formed from the remains of plants and animals that died millions of years ago.

When people burn these fossil fuels, **the pollutants from the fuels are released into the atmosphere.** Here are some examples:

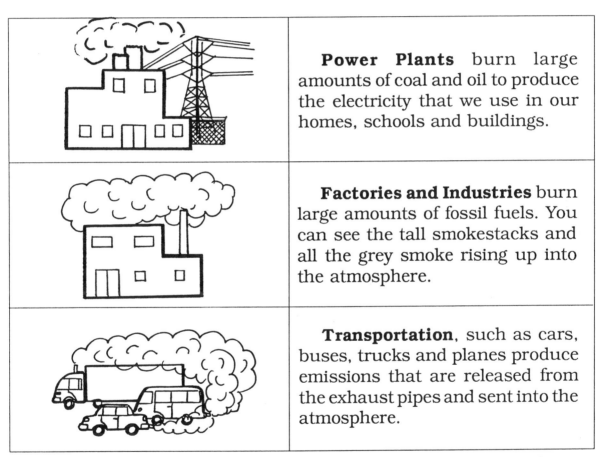

	Power Plants burn large amounts of coal and oil to produce the electricity that we use in our homes, schools and buildings.
	Factories and Industries burn large amounts of fossil fuels. You can see the tall smokestacks and all the grey smoke rising up into the atmosphere.
	Transportation, such as cars, buses, trucks and planes produce emissions that are released from the exhaust pipes and sent into the atmosphere.

In the pictures, color the smoke (the pollutants) that are being released into the atmosphere.

Acid rain results from burning _____, _____ and

_____.

They are called _____.

Which Pictures Do Not Cause Pollutants?

Coal, oil and natural gas (the fossil fuels) create the pollutants that cause acid rain.
Color the pictures that DO NOT cause pollutants in the atmosphere.
Cross out (X) the pictures that do cause pollutants to rise into the atmosphere.

What Are The "ACIDS" in Acid Rain?

The two main pollutants that come from burning fossil fuel *(coal, oil and natural gas)* are:

---

1) sulfur dioxide - SO_2
2) nitrogen oxide - NO_x

These pollutants (SO_2 and NO_x) can turn into acid rain when they are released into the atmosphere. When the pollutants are in the atmosphere they mix with water vapor and react with sunlight. When this happens it produces a chemical reaction which turns:

1) sulfer dioxide (SO_2) into sulfuric acid
2) nitrogen oxide (NO_X) into nitric acid.

These acids become part of the water vapor that condenses and forms clouds. The polluting acids which come from burning the fossil fuels in the power plants, cars and factories are now in the clouds.

Eventually, the water becomes too heavy and falls to earth as acid rain.

Burning fossil fuels creates the pollutants which rise into the atmosphere. These pollutants (sulfuric acid and nitric acid) form with the water in the clouds and then falls to earth as acid rain. (COLOR THE PICTURE.)

Acid Rain Isn't Always Wet!

Acid rain falls to earth in two form.

1) WET DEPOSITION is the term used when acid rain falls to earth in rain, snow, sleet, hail, frost, dew and mist.

2) DRY DEPOSITION is when the acids fall to earth as tiny particles or dust.

Draw a picture showing all the ways that acid rain can fall to earth. Label each part of your picture.

Catching Air Particles - Experiments!

Although we are not as aware of the **DRY DEPOSITION** that is occurring in our environment, there are some experiments that we can do to help us see the "invisible" particles or dust.

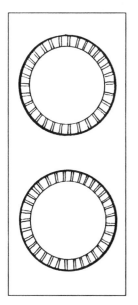

VERSION I - Paper Plates

You Will Need: 2 heavy white paper plates and petroleum jelly.

What You Do: Cover each plate with petroleum jelly. Put the plates outside on a window ledge or someplace where they will not be blown away. Leave one plate outside for one day. Leave the other plate outside for at least one week. Compare the two plates.

The students will enjoy comparing the two paper plates and recording their findings.

The students might also enjoy performing this experiment in different locations. The plates could be left near a factory, near their homes, a park, etc. The students could then record their finding at each of the different locations and compare the differences or similarities of all the paper plates.

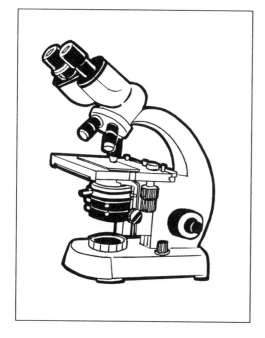

VERSION II - Microscope

The experience of observing dry particles in the air can be greatly enhanced with the use of a microscope.

Instead of using the paper plates, follow the same instructions using microscope slides. Viewing the slides under a microscope will enable the students to see size, color and quantity differences more closely.

Acid Rain Can Travel Long Distances!

No one likes air pollution! No one likes to live near air pollution! And no one wants to breathe air that is polluted! For years people have complained about "smog" and "smoke-filled" air. This type of air pollution is especially noticable in large cities.

(Discuss with your class air pollution in large cities.
Show the children pictures of air pollution and factories with large smokestacks.)

To combat the air pollution problem, primarily in large cities, factories began building taller and taller smokestacks. Some of these smokestacks are over fifty stories high. The reason for doing this did make some sense at first. People thought if we make the smoke go up very high, then we would not smell it or breathe it on earth. We thought we would be able to keep the air we breathe clean. The tall smokestacks would be sending the smoke up so high that it would not bother us.

Unfortunately, by building these smokestacks so high, we ended up sending the smoke, filled with the pollutants, even higher into the atmosphere. The wind then carries the pollutants to places very far away from where the smoke and pollutants first began. In other words, some of the pollutants in Mexico are carried into the United States, and the pollutants from the Midwest states are carried into New England and Canada.

Since we have learned that the pollutants from the smokestacks create acid rain, we now know that we are causing it to rain acid rain in many other parts of the world.

Lets Try To See The "ACID" In Some Science Experiments

The word "acid" means "sour." Some of the foods we eat have acids in them, like oranges, limes, lemons and grapefruits. The acid found in these fruits is called **citric acid.** It is the citric acid which makes these fruits sometimes taste sour. Citric acids do not hurt us.

But stronger acids which are the products of factories, industries and laboratories are very **POISONOUS!** Acids used in batteries, fertilizers, and many other products are also very poisonous.

You can measure the acid in many things by using inexpensive pHydrion papers *(pH papers).* You can usually get some from your local high school chemistry teacher or you can write to one of the following addresses:

Carolina Biological Supply Company
Box 187
Gladestone, Oregon 97027

Medical Center Surgical Supply Company
344 Longwood Avenue
Boston, Massachusettes 02115

THE EXPERIMENTS

pH paper is easy to use. Dip the paper into a solution. Depending upon the amount of acid in the solution the pH paper will turn different colors. A color chart is included with the pH papers so you can compare the color of the pH paper to the chart.

Once you have purchased your pH papers you can go ahead and perform a variety of experiments. The following is a list of everyday things which the children can test for the pH value. Provide the children with the reproducible chart on the following page. The children can use this chart for recording their findings.

(Approximate answer key for the teacher)	
Lemon Juice	2.0
Vinegar	2.2
Apples	3.0
Pears	3.8
Tomatoes	4.2
Carrots	5.0
Milk	6.6
Pure Water	7.0

KEEP IN MIND

Normal Rain has a pH value *ABOVE 5.0*

Acid Rain has any pH value *BELOW 5.0*

Healthy Lake Water has a pH value *BETWEEN 6.0 to 8.0*

pH Paper Experiment Recording Chart

REMEMBER
Normal Rain has a pH value **ABOVE** _____
Acid Rain has a pH value **BELOW** _____
Healthy Lake Water has a pH value **BETWEEN** _____ to _____

Use your pH papers to test for the pH value in the following things.
Record your findings. Compare your findings with a partner.

Lemon Juice _____

Vinegar _____

Apples _____

Pears _____

Tomatoes _____

Carrots _____

Milk _____

Water _____

Acid Rain In Our Lakes

Acid rain is having a serious effect on our lakes. Scientists and biologists first became aware that some of our lakes were in trouble when they noticed a decreasing number of fish. The scientists suspected that the problem might be acid rain. The scientists began measuring the pH value of the water in these lakes and discovered that some of these lakes had a high "acid" value and were being damaged by acid rain.

From this information the scientists began to study the effect that acid rain was having on all aquatic life *(animals who live in and on the water)*. They learned that different animals were able to tolerate different levels of acid in the water.

A WATER EXPERIMENT

Here is an experiment that you can perform which will help you understand what is happening to the water in some of our lakes.

You Will Need: a large clear glass bowl
distilled water (purchased at any grocery store)
pH paper
baking soda
vinegar
pencil
reproducible chart on the following page

1. Fill the bowl with the distilled water. Test the pH value. It should be somewhere between 5.6 and 7.0. If it is below 7.0, add baking soda(an alkaline), just a little bit at a time, until the pH reaches 7.0. Once the water is 7.0 you have the perfect pH value for clear, healthy lake water. It is in this water that **all** aquatic life can thrive and live well.

2. Now add small amounts of vinegar. Each time you add vinegar measure the pH value. ***On the reproducible chart on the following page compare which aquatic life has suffered due to the increased acid in the water.***
Continue adding small amounts of vinegar until you have reached a 4.5 or lower pH value. It is at a 4.5 pH value that most all aquatic life has died.

(This experiment is an excellent cooperative learning activity. Divide the class into groups of 4 to 6 children.)

Effects of Acid Rain on Aquatic Life Chart

(Use with Water Experiment on page 17.)

The Effects Of Acid Rain On Aquatic Life

	pH 6.5	pH 6.0	pH 5.5	pH 5.0	pH 4.5	pH 4.0	pH 3.5
Brook Trout	fish	fish	fish	fish	outline		
Yellow Perch	fish	fish	fish	fish	outline		
Bullfrog	tadpole	tadpole	tadpole	tadpole	outline		
American Toad	frog	frog	frog	frog	outline		
Spotted Salamander	salamander	salamander	salamander	outline			
Brown Trout	fish	fish	fish	outline			
Rainbow Trout	fish	fish	outline				
Smallmouth Bass	fish	fish	outline				
Pumpkinseed Sunfish	fish	fish	fish	outline			
Crayfish	crayfish	crayfish	outline				
Mayfly	mayfly	mayfly	outline				
Snail	snail	outline					
Clam	clam	outline					
Fathead Minnow	fish	outline					

Most aquatic life can tolerate water with a pH range of between 6.5 to 9.5. When the pH falls to below 6.0 we begin to see damage to aquatic life. **The white outline shows when each first becomes affected by acid rain.**

 Treat The Earth Gently

What Is Happening To Our Forests?

Scientists began to notice a decline in our forests between 1950 and 1960. The scientists are not sure if the forest decline is due to acid rain, but they are suspicious that acid rain is the cause.

It was easy to measure the pH value in the water in the lakes, but it is much more difficult to determine exactly why our forests are having problems. It is curious to note that our country began burning many fossil fuels between the years 1950 and 1960. This is the same time period that the decline in the forests was first observed.

It also seems to make sense that if acid rain can damage the water in our lakes that it could also damage the soil in which our trees grow.

SOIL EXPERIMENT

Here is a fun experiment that may help you see the effect that acid rain may be having on the soil in some of our forests.

You will need: Radish seeds; bean seeds; potting soil; pH paper; 12 paper cups; vinegar; baking soda; water; measuring cups.

1. Fill all 12 paper cups with potting soil. Leave one-half to one inch of space at the top of each cup.

2. Mark 4 cups with the letter "A." Mark 4 cups with the letter "B." Mark 4 cups with the letter "C."

3. Plant 2 "A" cups with several radish seeds.
   Plant 2 "A" cups with several bean seeds.
   Plant 2 "B" cups with several radish seeds.
   Plant 2 "B" cups with several bean seeds.
   Plant 2 "C" cups with several radish seeds.
   Plant 2 "C" cups with several bean seeds.
Then place all the cups in a sunny place.

Soil Experiment Continued

4. Each group of cups will be watered with a different type of water:

Group "A" - Add vinegar to tap water until you get a pH of 4.0. Test with your pH paper.

Group "B" - In a different measuring cup, add baking soda to tap water until you get a pH of 8.0. Test with your pH paper.

Group "C" - Water these cups with plain tap water.

SPECIAL NOTE: Always water each group of seeds with the same amount of water. (1/4 cup should be sufficient.) Water whenever the soil seems dry.

REMEMBER
Group "A" always gets the pH 4.0 water.
Group "B" always gets the pH 8.0 water.
Group "C" always gets the plain tap water.

Observe your seedlings for several weeks.
• *Which plants sprouted first?*
• *Which seedlings grew the fastest?*
• *Do you think acid rain could have an effect on how the trees in our forests are growing?*

(This is an excellent activity for the children to graph or to record daily observations. Use the reproducible chart on the following page.)

Soil Experiment
Daily Recording & Observation Chart

	pH 4.0 Water				pH 8.0 Water				Tap Water			
	A	A	A	A	B	B	B	B	C	C	C	C
	Radish	Radish	Bean	Bean	Radish	Radish	Bean	Bean	Radish	Radish	Bean	Bean
Day 1												
Day 2												
Day 3												
Day 4												
Day 5												
Day 6												
Day 7												
Day 8												
Day 9												
Day 10												
Day 11												
Day 12												
Day 13												
Day 14												
Day 15												
Day 16												
Day 17												
Day 18												
Day 19												
Day 20												

Record any observations you make while performing the soil experiment. Here is a recording system that may help you:

Write "**S**" = Seeds Sprouted
Write "**N**" = Noticable Growth
Write "**D**" = Seeds or Plant Died

On the back of this paper write any other observations you made. For example;
- Were there any color differences between the plants?
- Did the radishes grow faster than the beans?
- Which group, A, B or C sprouted first?
- Which plants look to be the healthiest?
- Which plants have the best color?
- Did any of the plants die?
- Did any of the cups have seeds that did not grow at all?

 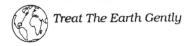

WORD HUNT

Circle all the words in the puzzle that are in the word bank.

```
Q  C  K  L  A  K  E  S  A  N  P  G  F
Z  O  L  H  T  B  F  D  C  O  B  C  O
Y  A  G  C  M  G  I  K  I  X  L  F  S
B  L  J  P  O  L  L  U  T  A  N  T  S
C  Q  M  J  S  P  L  T  H  C  Q  J  I
P  H  P  A  P  E  R  S  D  I  A  R  L
H  W  Z  T  H  Q  M  V  J  D  M  Q  F
C  F  O  R  E  S  T  S  K  R  D  L  U
O  I  D  U  R  X  P  O  F  A  N  S  E
M  S  Q  W  E  T  Q  2  O  I  L  K  L
N  H  R  V  D  R  Y  A  L  N  C  T  S
```

Word Bank

FOSSIL FUELS	LAKES
ACID RAIN	COAL
POLLUTANTS	OIL
ATMOSPHERE	WET
PH PAPERS	DRY
FORESTS	NO_x
FISH	SO_2

MY ACID RAIN REPORT

If someone asked you to tell them about acid rain, what would you say?
Write down what you might say.

_____

_____

_____

_____

_____

_____

_____

_____

_____

_____

_____

_____

_____

Unit 2
OZONE

CONTENTS

Ozone - Is It Good Or Bad?

Ozone is a word that we frequently hear and read about in the news. The term ozone can be difficult to understand because it has more than one meaning. Sometimes the word **ozone** sounds like something terrible; other times the word **ozone** sounds like something that we cannot live without. So - what is ozone? Is it something bad? Is is something good? Do we need it? Should we try to get rid of it?

The surprise is that ozone is something that is both good and bad for all living things.

Here is a brief description of the difference. Study the pictures to help you understand which "ozone" is being talked about on the following pages.

The "Bad" Ozone
Ozone can be a toxic gas called smog. Smog is an air pollutant that stays close to the earth's surface and affects the air that we breath.
This is bad.

The "Good" Ozone
Way up in the stratosphere, about 15 to 20 miles above the earth, ozone happens naturally and protects the earth. It blocks out the harmful ultraviolet rays from the sun.
This is good.

In the following lessons the children will be taking a closer look at both forms of ozone.

The "Bad" Ozone - A Pollutant!

You have learned from lesson 1 that ozone can be a toxic gas that is commonly called "smog." Smog, or the toxic gas called ozone, is an air pollutant that is created by burning fossil fuels. *(Remember, coal, oil and natural gas that you learned about in the Acid Rain unit.)*

The main chemical reaction that creates ozone occurs when we mix 3 main ingredients:

• The two main components of air - nitrogen and oxygen, in high temperatures form **NITROGEN OXIDES.**

• **HYDROCARBONS**, which come from the exhaust tailpipes of cars and trucks.

• **SUNLIGHT.**

When one mixes the **NITROGEN OXIDES, HYDROCARBONS** and **SUNLIGHT** the result is **OZONE.** When this occurs close to the earth we can actually see smog. Not only can we see the smog, but it can irritate our eyes, burn our throats and can cause damage to our forests and crops.

Cars and trucks emit more than half of the smog or ozone producing chemicals. These chemicals are released through the exhaust tailpipes of cars, trucks, buses, and other transportation vehicles.

CAR-OF-THE-FUTURE

Since cars and trucks produce so much smog, wouldn't it be exciting if we could design a car that didn't need to be fueled with gas. In the space below design a Car-Of-The-Future that does not burn gas.

Another fun art activity is to use old shoe boxes and scrap materials to design a car-of-the-future. Using "throw-aways" in art projects is a form of recycling.

Cars Are Not The Only Guilty Culprits!

Most air pollution or smog is caused by people burning things, such as the gas burning in the engine of a car and then being relased through the exhaust tailpipes of the car. But there are many other things which create air pollution such as:

- **Fireplaces**
- **Lawn Mowers**
- **Barbeques**
- **Jet Engines**
- **Factories**

CLASS ACTIVITY

Brainstorm together as a class and make a list of everything that you can think of which may create air pollution.

AN EXPERIMENT

Some air pollution we can easily see in the air, while some other forms of air pollution are not so easy to see.

Light a candle in your classroom. Ask a volunteer to blow out the flame on the candle. Can you see the smoke float through the air? Where does the smoke go when you can no longer see it?

Next, light the candle again. Hold a glass lid *(the lid from a Pyrex dish works well)* over the flame. *(The teacher should be the one who holds the lid. Be sure to use a potholder.)* After a few minutes you will notice a black spot forming on the lid. As the candle burned it released gases (pollution) that settled on the glass.

We can visibly see many forms of air pollution, but there are also forms of air pollution that we cannot see. Some of the chemicals that create invisible forms of air pollution are found in everyday household products.

- **Glass Cleaners**
- **Some aerosal anti-perspirants**
- **Oil-based paints use chemical solvents for clean-up**

What Can We Do?

There are many things that we can do to help decrease air pollution. Bring this list home and go over it with your parents.

1. Make sure that your car is in good working order. Have a tune-up, check the spark plugs and change the oil.

2. Car pool whenever you can. (Athletic teams, girl scouts, music classes; whenever possible, team-up and car pool.)

3. Use mass transit, or ever better walk, ride a bike, or rollerskate. The exercise is better for all of us too!

4. Don't ever leave your car idling. It is not safe to leave a car running when you are not in it, and it is a major contributor to air pollution.

5. Write a shopping list. How often do we go to the store and forget an item and then drive back to the store again. Plan ahead so you only need to make one trip to the store.

6. Shop wisely. Read labels and become aware of products that are environmentally safe.

7. A fire in a fireplace is a beautiful thing to watch, but it can also add to air pollution. Be smart when you are using the fireplace. Never burn wet or green wood. Be sure that the wood is very dry. Place wood in a sheltered place to completely dry out before it is used in a fire. Save building fires for special occasions only.

Make a list at home with your parents of all the things that you can do as a family to reduce down air pollution. Be a solution to the problem and not part of the problem!

The "Good" Ozone - A Protector

The "bad" ozone that you just learned about in the preceding lesson was created by people and stays close to the earth.

The "good" ozone is not made by people, but rather is naturally produced high above the earth.

Up in the stratosphere, some 15 to 20 miles above the earth's surface there is a strong-smelling gas called **OZONE.** This naturally made ozone is like a shield protecting the earth from the sun's **ULTRAVIOLET (UV) RAYS.** The ozone shield allows the suns warming rays to come down to earth, but filters out the ultraviolet (UV) rays which can be very dangerous to living things. We are very lucky to have this layer of ozone to protect all of us!

Below is a picture of our earth. Color the earth. Draw the ozone layer around the earth. Draw the sun. Draw the sun's rays and show how the ozone layer allows the warming rays to enter and filters out the ultraviolet rays.

Oh No! Disappearing Ozone!

For many years scientists have been suspicious that parts of our protective ozone layer were disappearing. In the mid-1980's the scientists suspicions were confirmed - parts of the ozone layer are disappearing and becoming thin. This is called **OZONE DEPLETION.**

They first noticed that ozone depletion was occurring over **Antarctica** and spreading toward South America, New Zealand and Australia. Researchers originally believed that the ozone was only thinning over Antarctica.

Later, researchers learned that the ozone is also thinning over the **Arctic** which affects Europe, North America, and the Soviet Union.

On the map of the world find and color the following areas:

- South America
- New Zealand
- Australia
- Antarctica
- Arctic
- Europe
- North America
- Soviet Union

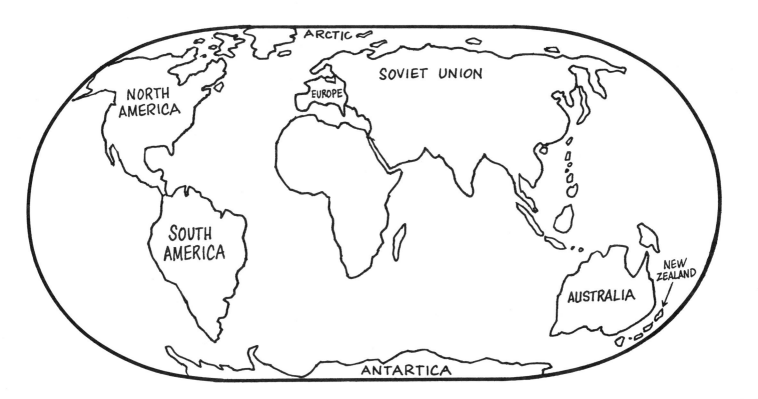

Isn't it amazing how much of the world is affected by ozone depletion!

Why Is Ozone Depletion Harmful?

Remember, the job of the ozone layer is to shield out the harmful ultraviolet rays from the sun. When the ozone layer becomes thin, more and more ultraviolet rays reach the earth's surface. These ultraviolet sun rays could cause four major areas of damage.

HEALTH OF PEOPLE

UV rays increase the potential for skin cancer and eye cataracts. It is also possible that a depleted ozone layer could make people more vulnerable to a variety of infectious diseases.

FOOD AND CROPS

UV rays could greatly affect our food chain. It is possible that UV rays could mutate and eventually destroy our crops of fruits and vegetables. This would also affect how much food we would have to feed livestock.

OCEAN LIFE

The UV rays could destroy tiny organisms that are necessary for the survival of all ocean life. In the waters of Antarctica we have already seen some changes and damage due to the sun's ultraviolet rays.

CLIMATE/WEATHER

The depletion of the ozone layer could also cool the stratosphere layer of the atmosphere. This would create changes in the wind patterns that would change our weather. Drastic weather changes could affect all living things.

Why Is The Ozone Layer Disappearing?

This serious problem of ozone depletion has one major villian -
CFC's. - (CHLOROFLUOROCARBONS)

Some of the other names for CFC's are:
- Halons, carbon tetrachloride and methyl chloroform
  - Trichlorofluoromethane (CFC-11)
  - Dichlorodifluoromethane (CFC-12)
  - Trichlorotrifluoroethane (CFC-13)
  - Dichlorotetrafluoroethane (CFC-14)

It is easier to remember CFC than to remember chlorofluorocarbons. From now on in the reading the chlorofluorocarbons will be referred to as CFC's.

CFC's were made by humans in the 1930's. When CFC's were originally discovered people were thrilled! People thought they had finally found "wonder chemical." CFC's have

- **no odor**
- **are not flammable**
- **are noncorrosive, and**
- **are nontoxic.**

In other words, people believed that they had found a chemical that would not hurt anyone or anything. Since people believed that this chemical was so safe and could do so many things, it was put in a huge variety of products.

- **CFC's are in refrigerator cooling systems**
- **CFC's are used to clean computer and electronic equipment**
- **CFC's are in home insulation**
- **CFC's are in foam "throw-away" food containers (*egg cartons, cups*)**
- **CFC's are in some aerosol cans (*although the U.S. no longer allows CFC's in aerosol products*)**
- **CFC's are in the air conditioners of cars and other vehicles**
- **CFC's are in fire extinguishers**
- **CFC's are in packing foam. (*The foam pieces that are put in packages that are mailed*)**
- **CFC's are in building air conditioners**
- **CFC's are in sterilants (*often used in hospitals*)**

 *Treat the Earth Gently*

CFC's Are Eating The Protective Ozone Layer

CFC's seemed like a very safe chemical for humans while it was on the earth's surface. But, it has been discovered that CFC's are leaving the earth's surface and drifting up to the earth's stratosphere *(where the protective ozone layer is found)*. When CFC's reach the stratosphere the ultraviolet radiation from the sun changes CFC's from a once safe chemical into an **ozone-eating monster.**

Study and color the picture. Can you see all the products that CFC's are used in? Can you see the CFC's entering the stratosphere and changing into ozone eating monsters?

Make a list of all the products
that you can think of that contain CFC's.

_____

_____

_____

_____

_____

_____

_____

_____

_____

_____

_____

_____

_____

_____

This is an excellent cooperative learning activity. Divide the children into groups of 4 to 6 and have them cooperatively think of products that contain CFC's.

What Can We Do To Help The Ozone Layer?

Aerosol Spray Cans

People are trying to correct the problem of CFC's, but it is not easy. The United States, Canada and several Scandinavian countries banned the use of aerosol sprays that contained CFC's in 1978. But many other countries still use CFC's in their aerosol spray products. Some of these countries are France, Japan, and many countries in Eastern Europe. Aerosol spray cans are still the largest producer of CFC's in the world. Aerosol spray cans possibly contribute up to one-third of the ozone-eating chemical.

In 1989, 81 nations announced they would ban the production and use of CFC's by the year 2000. The United States was one of those countries.

Foam Products

Many restaurants use foam cups, plates, and food containers. Some grocery products are packaged with foam. Still, other products are put in cardboard boxes that are filled with foam chips or pieces to protect whatever is in the box. Be alert to white foam. We can help our environment by not purchasing products that contain CFC's or products that are packaged in CFC containing materials. Look for packages that say: **"NON-CFC."**

If you are not sure if the foam packages, cups, plates, and other products you are buying contain CFC's, it's a good idea not to buy them. Check the list on page 35 before purchasing questionable items.

REMEMBER: **CFC's are safe when they are secure in their plastic foam. The CFC's are released into the atmosphere when the plastic foam is broken and thrown-away.**

Air Cooling and Air Conditioning

Help your parents remember to safety check their refrigerators and car air conditioning systems. Any leaks in either of these is probably sending CFC's into our atmosphere.

What To Use Instead Of CFC In Products?

The problem is not only getting people to stop using CFC's in manufacturing and packaging products, but the problem is also what should people be using instead of CFC's.

Many large companies are working very hard to discover through research another safe chemical that they can use instead of CFC's. So far, no one has found that chemical.

─────────────── **CFC AWARENESS POSTER** ───────────────

Design a poster that will encourage people not to use CFC containing products. Think up a catchy slogan. Display your posters around school. Use recycled paper for your poster or use the blank side of an already used sheet of paper.

How Much Have You Learned?

1. The ozone layer is found _____ miles above the earth.

2. Ozone can be a toxic gas called _____.

3. The ozone layer blocks out the sun's harmful _____rays.

4. Smog irritates our _____ and burns our _____.

5. Most air pollution is caused by people _____ things.

6. _____ _____ means the thinning of the ozone layer.

7. There is a huge hole in the ozone layer over _____.

8. CFC is short for _____.

9. _____, _____ and _____ all contain CFC's.

10. Name a country that will ban all CFC's by the year 2000. _____.

WORD BANK			
United States	ultraviolet	eyes	Antarctica
15 to 20	chlorofluorocarbon	throat	refrigerators
Smog	ozone depletion	burning	aerosols
			foam products

Unit 3
GLOBAL WARMING

CONTENTS

Is The Earth Really Getting Warmer?

**Is the earth really getting warmer?
It sure is and we are trying to understand why!**

Have you ever walked through a greenhouse? Most communities have nurseries *(a place where plants and flowers are grown and sold)*. Nurseries have special buildings called **greenhouses** where plants are grown. It feels very warm in a greenhouse because the heat is not allowed to leave and sunlight is always shining through the glass walls. The temperature in a greenhouse is carefully controlled so plants are able to grow as healthy as possible.

Many people believe that our earth is growing warmer because of the **GREENHOUSE EFFECT.** The Greenhouse Effect is a theory that says that we are sending many gases (pollutants) into the atmosphere. These gases let the sun's radiation in but do not let the heat back out. It is just like the earth is sitting in the middle of a giant greenhouse.

If we could control the amount of heat and sun on earth, just as it is controlled in a greenhouse, we wouldn't have a problem. But, we are not able to regulate the earth's temperature. The possibility of the earth becoming warmer could cause some serious problems. This problem is called **GLOBAL WARMING.**

So - Who Cares
If The Earth Is Getting Warmer?

So - Who cares if the earth is getting warmer?
WE SHOULD!!!

Scientists are not sure what would happen if the earth kept getting warmer. Many scientists feel that a warmer earth would dramatically change our climate. Some of these scientists feel that we should call this **"Global Climate Change"** instead of **"Global Warming."**

Climate changes may be so unpredictable that scientists really don't know what might happen. They are using computers to try and help them form better judgements. Right now all we have are educated guesses.

If the earth's climate becomes warmer it could affect the earth in many ways:

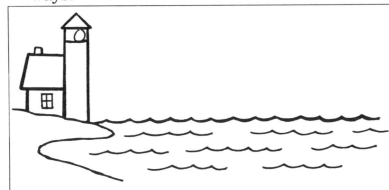

OCEANS
Warmer weather could begin to melt the ice in Antarctica. This melted ice would cause the water level in the oceans to rise. A dramatic rise in the ocean water levels could cause flooding.

FARMING
Land, especially in the Midwest area of the United States could become too hot and dry for growing crops.

WILDLIFE
If there is a climate change some animals may not be affected; others would move to areas where the climate is better suited for their survival; and some species would surely die.

Draw a picture that shows how you think the earth would change if it became warmer. Write some sentences telling about your picture.

What Are The Gases That Create The Greenhouse Effect?

Now that we know that Global Warming could present some serious problems, let's take a look at why this is happening.

There are a great many gases that are helping to create the Greenhouse Effect. Several of the worst culprits you already know about if you have completed the Acid Rain and Ozone units.

FOSSIL FUELS

When fossil fuels are burned *(coal, oil and natural gas)* it produces **CARBON DIOXIDE.**

It is suggested that 50% of the gases that are keeping the heat close to the earth are **CARBON DIOXIDE** gases.

The carbon dioxide gases that are released from the burning of fossil fuels is the major contributor to the Greenhouse Effect, which is creating Global Warming.

Here are some of the things that burn fossil fuels which release carbon dioxide:

- Incenerators
- Electric Power Plants
- Household Furnances
- Waste Treatment Plants
- Factories
- Cars and Buses

METHANE is another gas that is adding to the Greenhouse Effect. It comes from:

- Landfills
- Flooded Rice Paddies
- Dead Animals
- Termits
- Burning Wood
- Burning Fossil Fuels

NITROUS OXIDE is another gas that contributes to the Greenhouse Effect and is produced by burning fossil fuels. This gas often comes from:

- Gasoline
- Some Nitrogen-Based Fertilizers

Fill in the missing letters to help you remember some of the Greenhouse Effect Gases.

C _ R _ O _ D _ _ X _ _ E

_ E _ _ AN _

N _ TR _ _ S _ X _ _ _ _

OZONE

High in the atmosphere the ozone layer protects us from the sun's ultra-violet rays, but remember that close to earth ozone is a pollutant. The low-level polluting ozone functions as one of the gases that is contributing to the Greenhouse Effect.

CFC's - CHLOROFLUOROCARBONS

CFC's are man-made chemicals that are eating away the protective ozone layer. Not only are CFC's destroying the ozone layer but they are also contributing to the Greenhouse Effect which is creating Global Warming.

Carbon Dioxide						50%				
Methane			20%							
CFC's		15%								
Nitrogen Oxides	10%									
Low-Level Ozone	5%									

Source: Natural Resources Defense Council; Inform, Inc.; *The Challenge of Global Warming*, ed. Dean Edwin Abrahamson. Washington: Island Press, 1989.

CLASS PROJECT

As a class project make a list of all the things that you can think of that contribute to Global Warming.

Plant A Tree

We have learned that the fossil fuels that produce CARBON DIOXIDE are the major contributors to the Greenhouse Effect, which is causing Global Warming. We have also learned that there are many other gases and chemicals, such as low-level ozone and CFC's, that contribute to the Greenhouse Effect.

There is another major factor in the Greenhouse Effect - TREES!!!

Trees, especially the tropical Rain Forests, absorb carbon dioxide from the atmosphere. This is good. The more trees there are, the more carbon dioxide they will absorb and help our earth to maintain a natural balance.

Since trees act as a warehouse of carbon dioxide, when they are burned or even cut down, they release carbon dioxide into the atmosphere.

In other words - **WHEN TREES ARE LIVING AND FOUND IN ABUNDANCE THEY HELP THE ENVIRONMENT! WHEN A TREE IS DESTROYED IT ADDS TO THE PROBLEM.**

Repair This Forest!
Draw And Color Many Trees.

PLANT A TREE

Plant a tree on your school grounds. *(Plant more than one tree if possible!) You might encourage a nursery to donate a tree to your school.*

Review Of The Possible Causes Of Global Warming

Add other pictures to the earth which contribute to the Greenhouse Effect.

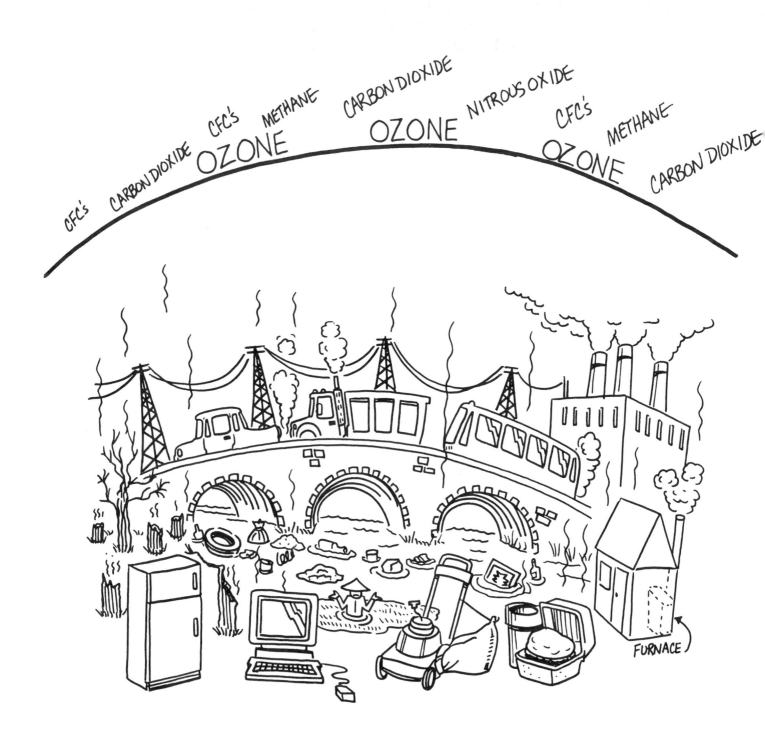

School Patrol

**Take a walk through your school and make a list of all the things that
you can find which might be damaging to our earth.
Which things use fossil fuels?
Which things may contain CFC's?**

Missing Letters Puzzle

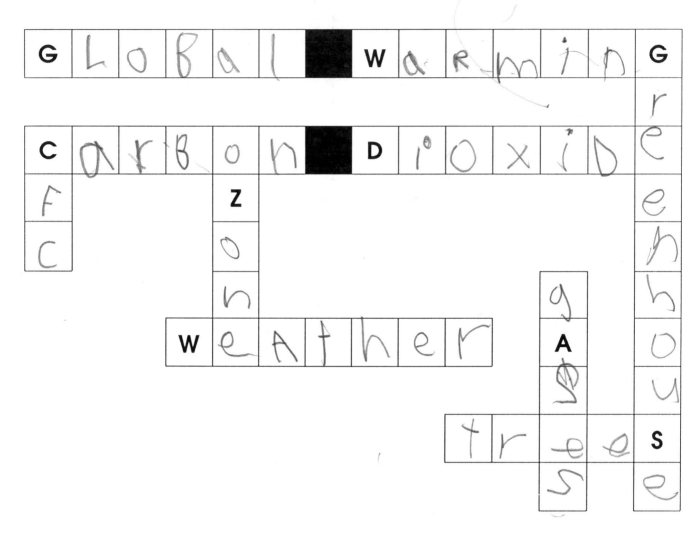

Use the word bank to fill in all the missing letters in the above puzzle.

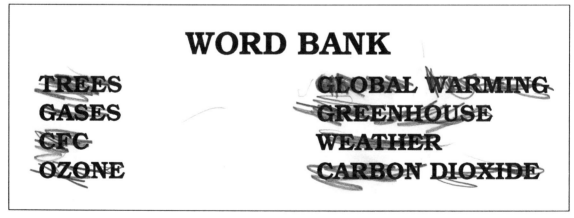

WORD BANK

TREES   GLOBAL WARMING

GASES   GREENHOUSE

CFC   WEATHER

OZONE   CARBON DIOXIDE

A Challenge Activity: On the back of your paper, try to write a definition of each of the words in the word bank.

Unit 4

GARBAGE OVERLOAD

CONTENTS

Where Should All The Garbage Go?
To A Landfill?

DO WE REALLY HAVE A GARBAGE OVERLOAD PROBLEM?

We sure do and everyone is talking about it! We are throwing away too much and we're running out of places to put it.

In the United States we throw away about 5 billion tons of trash each year. We throw away everything from refrigerators, to bottles, tires, clothes, furniture, food, broken toys, household chemicals, paper, newspapers, glass, etc. The list of what we throw away is endless!

Have you ever stood on your street the day that your garbage is collected? If you haven't, you should! Take a look at all the garbage just from the homes on your street! Trash cans, huge plastic bags filled to the top, old boxes, appliances, and hopefully some recycling containers. Where does all that garbage go?

IN THE PAST . . .

We had places called **DUMPS.** A Dump was a place where people put garbage. Dumps were often located in or by sinkholes and swamplands. Garbage was "dumped" into a large hole. In this type of open dump there were many problems with pests, such as rats and flies.

Another serious problem of a dump was that the garbage often polluted surface water and ground water. At many dumps, it was common to burn the garbage which added to the problems of air pollution.

Where Should All The Garbage Go? - con't

NOW-A-DAYS . . .

We have places called **LANDFILLS.** Landfills are an improvement from the dumps of the past. A landfill is a hole in the ground that is lined with clay or plastic. The garbage is put in the landfill, spread out, compacted daily and then covered with a layer of dirt or plastic. Covering the garbage each day helps control the pests and helps to decrease fires.

When a landfill is designed properly and operated well it will reduce the amount of contaminants that reach our surface and ground water.

BUT . . .

Our landfills are filling up fast! All across the country we are seeing more and more "closed" signs. Should we build more landfills? Unfortunately, it is difficult to find places to build new landfills. Farm land is often the best land for a landfill. But, do we want to sacrifice good farming land for a landfill? Another new site factor is that people do not want landfills in their neighborhoods! *Would you?*

DISCUSS THE PROBLEM

So - as you can see, we have a garbage overload problem! What do you think we should do about the garbage problem? Talk about it as a class. Would you want a landfill in your neighborhood? Where would you build a landfill? Find out where the landfills in your area are located.

Reduce & Reuse - How Do We Do That?

Many of you have probably heard these words!

REDUCE - REUSE - RECYCLE

If everyone understood what these words really mean, we could greatly reduce our garbage overload problem.

REDUCE

Reduce simply means to stop throwing away so much trash! We could reduce the amount of trash we throw away by:

NOT BUYING DISPOSIBLE PRODUCTS

We have become a "disposible" society. Use it once and then throw it away! We throw away paper and plastic plates, cups, silverware, disposible diapers, paper towels, plastic garbage bags, products that come with excessive packagingand so much more!. Be careful when you shop!

REPAIR BROKEN THINGS

We often throw away broken things that could be repaired. How many times have we tossed out that toy, article of clothing, or some other object simply because it was easier to buy a new one rather than to have the broken object repaired.

REUSE

Be clever! Try and figure out all the ways that things can be reused and not thrown away. Here are some ideas for you:

REUSING THINGS AT HOME

We can reuse lots of things. Use both sides of a piece of paper, empty containers such as shoe boxes, egg cartons, and margarine tubs can be used for storing items. Lots of scrap and "throw-a-away" things make wonderful art projects.

OTHER PEOPLE MIGHT LIKE YOUR UNWANTED THINGS

Sometimes our trash can be someone else's treasure! Old clothes can be mended, furniture repaired and toys fixed. There are many shelters and social service organizations that are desperate for these types of items. There are many people who might want things that you no longer need or want.

FIGURE IT OUT!

How Would You <u>Reduce</u> or <u>Reuse</u> These Items?

Work with a partner. Decide how you would either reuse the following items or reduce using the items. Write what you would do? Share your ideas with the entire class. How many different ideas did the other children come up with?

Coat Hanger	Mayonnaise Jar	Grocery bag
Yogurt Container	Cereal Box	Paper Napkins
Paper Towels	Book	Bike

Recycle - The "How-To's"

RECYCLING - is when we sort our trash into categories, so that the trash can be made into new products. Recycling can significantly reduce the amount of waste in our landfills!

We ususally sort our trash into these categories:

 Glass  Paper  Card board  Metal

Most communities now have recycling programs. Recycling centers typically accept cans, newspapers, and glass for recycling. Many recycling centers also accept other recyclable materials.

Many items that are commonly thrown out can be recycled!

METAL
- Scrap iron, copper, steel, aluminum and brass
- Aluminum trays
- Foil
- Tin cans
- Soda cans

GLASS
- Clear glass
- Green glass
- Brown glass

PAPER
- Newspaper
- Computer paper
- Office paper
- Envelopes
- Stationary
- Colored paper
- Index cards
- Brown paper bags
- Telephone books

PLASTIC
- Plastic is sorted by single type

HOUSEHOLD GOODS
- Furniture
- Appliances
- Clothes
- Toys
- Rags

CARDBOARD
- Brown corrugated cardboard
- Gray paperboard boxes
- Computer punch cards

―――――― **TIPS TO HELP YOU GET RECYCLING** ――――――

- Do not mix recyclable materials with other garbage.
- Find a good location to keep your recyclable materials - under a sink, in the garage, etc.
- Store each type of recyclable material in a separate container *(bag, box, shelf.)*
- **CANS** - Steel and aluminum cans should be separated. Remove any labels, rinse and crush the cans.
- **METAL** - Separate metals by type *(brass, copper, steel, aluminum.)*
- **GLASS** - Rinse glass jars and bottles well and separate according to color. Remove metal lids *(recycle the lids with the metals)*. Do not break the glass. *(Light bulbs, plate glass, and mirrors are not acceptable for recycling.)*
- **NEWSPAPER** - Tie with twine or put in boxes or brown paper bags.

―――――――――――――――――――――――――――――――――――――

LEARN TO SORT FOR RECYCLING!

Draw a line from the pictures to their correct recycling container.

MAKE A LIST OF RECYCLABLES

Think about all the things that you have seen thrown away. Make a list of all the things that you can think of that can either be
REDUCED, **REUSED** or **RECYCLED!**

REDUCE	REUSE	RECYCLE

Composting - Right In Your Own Backyard!

COMPOSTING is "organic" recycling.
Organic materials include:

- **Leaves**

- **Egg Shells**

- **Grass Clippings**

- **Sawdust**

- **Fruit and Vegetable Scraps**

- **Weeds**

- **Coffee Grounds**

- **Plant Trimmings**

These are things that come directly or indirectly from other living things.

Organic materials are broken down by living organisms and are biodegradable. **BIODEGRADABLE** means that these organic materials break down and return to the Earth.

Organic materials are broken down by scavengers such as beetles who feed on dead organisms. Later, **DECOMPOSERS**, like bacteria and fungi break down the materials even farther. As the organisms consume the organic materials it produces waste products that serve as nutrients for plants and other living things.

DO NOT USE THESE MATERIALS IN A COMPOST

- Meat
- Bones
- Grease
- Oil

- Fat
- Paper
- Large Branches
- Dairy Products
- Plastics

- Glass
- Synthetic Fibers
- Human or Pet Waste
- Diseased Plants

These materials can slow or stop the composting process.

 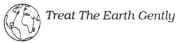

EXPERIMENT

Some trash such as organic materials break down and go back into the earth as nutrients that help keep our earth healthy. Other trash pollutes the earth. Here is an experiment that will help you discover which things are bio-degradable and which things stay in our landfills for many, many years.

TEAM WORK - *Divide your class equally into 3 or 4 teams.*

What Each Team Will Need:
- An area outside where it is okay to dig some holes. *(Hopefully you will find a location, such as under a tree, where there will be a lot of organisms.)*
- An Apple Core
- A Few Leaves
- Grass Clippings
- Plastic Bag
- Styrofoam Cup
- Glass Jar

What Each Team Will Do:
- Dig six holes, big enough to bury some of the above mentioned items.
- Bury one item in each hole.
- Make small signs to mark where you have buried your trash items.

- Wait 3 to 4 weeks and then go back and dig up the trash.

What did you find?
Fill out the chart below. Check your team's results with the other teams. Graph your findings.

Item	Condition of item after 3/4 weeks	Acceptable for a compost?
Apple Core		
Plastic bag		
Leaves		
Styrofoam Cup		
Grass		
Glass Jar		

How To Compost

It is easy to start a compost right in your own backyard!

1. Collect organic waste materials such as, leaves, grass, etc. *(Use the list on page 62.)* Collect these things in an inconspicuous spot out of the wind and direct sunlight.

2. Sprinkle a layer of soil over the top. This adds organisms that cause decay and helps to keep nutrients and moisture in the materials.

3. Be sure to water it until it a damp.

4. Enclose the materials with chicken wire, cement blocks or some kind of fence to ensure that you keep all the compost materials in one place.

5. Turn the materials every few days. Turning it more often will decrease the amount of composting time.

6. Add organic materials as they become available. Keep the compost watered and turn the materials. When the compost is dark and crumbles like soil it is ready for use.

PUTTING IT ALL TOGETHER!

We have learned that some of our trash is biodegradable and returns to the earth as something good. Some of our trash, even though it has been made from the earth's resources, does not break down and return anything good to the earth.

Somethings we can compost and somethings we need to recycle. Here is a long list of trash. What are you going to do with this trash? Should it be composted or recycled? Write the word **COMPOST** or **RECYCLE** next to each piece of trash.

Vegetable Can ⎯⎯⎯⎯⎯⎯⎯⎯⎯⎯ Mayonnaise Jar ⎯⎯⎯⎯⎯⎯⎯⎯⎯

Pop Bottle⎯⎯⎯⎯⎯⎯⎯⎯⎯⎯ Writing Paper ⎯⎯⎯⎯⎯⎯⎯⎯⎯

Newspaper ⎯⎯⎯⎯⎯⎯⎯⎯⎯ Orange Peels ⎯⎯⎯⎯⎯⎯⎯⎯⎯

Pile of Leaves ⎯⎯⎯⎯⎯⎯⎯⎯ Weeds⎯⎯⎯⎯⎯⎯⎯⎯⎯⎯⎯

Potato Skins ⎯⎯⎯⎯⎯⎯⎯⎯ Tuna Fish Can ⎯⎯⎯⎯⎯⎯⎯⎯

Sawdust ⎯⎯⎯⎯⎯⎯⎯⎯⎯⎯ Peanut Butter Jar ⎯⎯⎯⎯⎯⎯⎯

Soda Can ⎯⎯⎯⎯⎯⎯⎯⎯⎯⎯ Crab Apples ⎯⎯⎯⎯⎯⎯⎯⎯⎯

Coffee Grounds ⎯⎯⎯⎯⎯⎯⎯ Grass Clippings ⎯⎯⎯⎯⎯⎯⎯⎯

Cardboard Box ⎯⎯⎯⎯⎯⎯⎯ Telephone Book ⎯⎯⎯⎯⎯⎯⎯⎯

Egg Shells⎯⎯⎯⎯⎯⎯⎯⎯⎯⎯ Plant Trimmings ⎯⎯⎯⎯⎯⎯⎯

Incineration! - Burn! Burn!

Not only do we fill our landfills with waste, but we also burn a lot of waste. The process of burning waste is called **INCINERATION.**

As with all our solutions for solving the garbage overload problem, incineration has it's good points and it's bad points.

THE ADVANTAGES OF INCINERATING WASTE
"The Good Points"

• Energy in the form of electricity or steam for space heating is generated by incinerating garbage. This is called **WASTE-TO-ENERGY INCINERATION.** Some waste products that cannot be composted or recycled can be turned into useful steam heat and electricity.

• Incinerating trash greatly reduces the amount of trash put in a landfill. Incinerators can reduce the volume of the garbage by 60 to 90 percent, depending on how many materials are removed for recycling or composting.

• Incinerating trash reduces the problems of pests such as rats, roaches, flies, and other insects.

THE DISADVANTAGES OF INCINERATING WASTE
"The Bad Points"

It sounds fabulous that incinerating waste can produce energy and help reduce the amount of waste in our landfills. Unfortunately there are also some problems associated with incinerating waste.

• When waste is burned we are left with **ASH.** The remaining ash is put in landfills. Some of the ash is toxic. Toxic ash in a landfill can contaminate ground water. Ash needs to be buried in special areas of landfills.

• Smoke from incinerators may contain chemicals. Special air pollution equipment is necessary to control the air pollutants from incinerators.

• Some materials are more valuable when they are recycled. We need to be sure that Waste-To-Energy incineration is used together with recycling and composting.

• Incinerators are very expensive to build and operate.

What do you think about incinerating waste?

Hazardous Waste! - Oh Help!

What is Hazardous Waste?

To be classified as hazardous waste, the waste will have one or more of the following characteristics:

FLAMMABLE - a liquid, gas, or solid which could easily ignite and catch fire.

OXIDIZER - a waste which would supply oxygen to a fire. Fires need oxygen to burn.

CORROSIVE - a waste which is highly acidic or caustic.

EXPLOSIVE - waste materials that would react violently or produce toxic fumes when exposed to water - or waste materials that generate toxic gases when exposed to acidic or caustic conditions.

TOXIC TO ANIMALS - any waste materials that if an animal ate it, inhaled it, drank it, or came in contact with the skin would injure or kill the animal.

TOXIC CHEMICALS - which can be dissolved from the waste in an acidic environment.

The majority of hazardous waste is created by the chemical industry. But homes also contribute a large amount of hazardous waste each year. Look under your kitchen sink or out in your garage. You will find "everyday products" which will eventually turn into hazardous waste.

dyes	aerosol containers
batteries	motor oil
pesticides	kerosene
bathroom cleaning products	antifreeze
kitchen cleaning products	paint thinner
nail polish	chlorine bleach

GREENPEACE'S ALL-PURPOSE CLEANER RECIPE

1 Gallon Hot Water
1/4 cup Sudsy Ammonia
1/4 cup Vinegar
1 tablespoon Baking Soda

For heavier cleaning jobs
the recipe may be doubled.
WEAR GLOVES to protect your hands!

Better for the environment and less expensive!

In the preceding units you have learned that:

> **Acid rain** and **smog** are created by man-made chemicals,
>
> the protective layer of the **Ozone** is in danger
> because of man-made chemicals,
>
> **Global Warming** is happening because of the man-made
> chemicals causing the **Greenhouse Effect.**
>
> All these chemicals create **HARZARDOUS WASTE.**

If we reduce our use of products containing hazardous chemicals, we are not only helping to solve the hazardous waste disposal problems, but we are also helping in the fight against acid rain, the fight to help save the ozone layer, and in the fight to combat the potential dangers of global warming.

HOW CAN WE HELP WITH THE PROBLEMS OF HAZARDOUS WASTE

• We should stop purchasing products that contain hazardous chemicals. **(REDUCE)**

• Find out which products can be recycled. **(RECYCLE)**

• Find out about the Hazardous waste collection in your community, and follow the guidelines of that service.

• Do not dump any chemical down a sink or toilet.

I can save the earth by . . .

_____

_____

_____

_____

_____

_____

_____

_____

_____

_____

_____

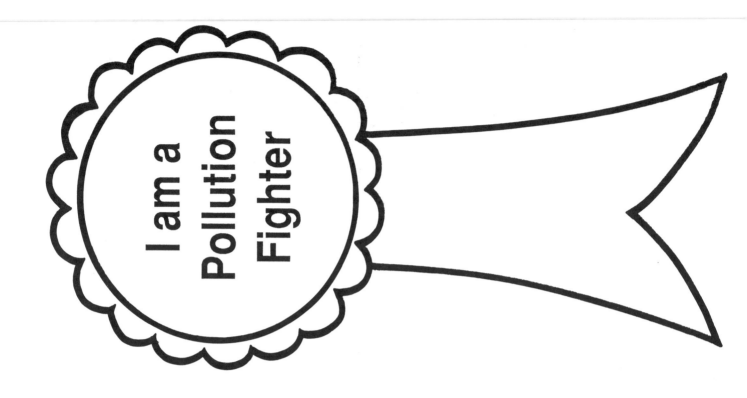

I am a Pollution Fighter

Recycling Award

I know how to recycle

PAPER CANS NEWS-PAPER GLASS

And it makes me proud!

Unit 5
ENERGY

CONTENTS

Too Many People Are Using Too Much Energy

Our use of energy is something that most of us take for granted. We jump in our cars and do not pay any attention to our excessive gasoline consumption and the pollution that the gasoline is creating. We leave lights on in our homes and buildings that do not need to be turned on. Everytime we turn on a light, or leave one on, we are using energy. We unnecessarily leave water running and use far too much hot water. The list could go on and on.

Our environmental problems of acid rain, smog, air pollution, water pollution, global warming, and our garbage overload perils are all created by our using **TOO MUCH ENERGY!**

90% *(and that's a lot!)* of the world's electricity comes from burning fossil fuels *(coal, oil, and natural gas)*. Remember from the preceding units all the environmental problems that are created by burning fossil fuels.

HOMEWORK ASSIGNMENT

A HOME ELECTRICITY STUDY. . .
Make a list of everything in your home that uses electricity. Bring your list to school. As a class combine the lists and make one giant list of everything that the children found.

CREATE SOME SOLUTIONS . . .
Next to each item that uses electricity, have the children decide how they could conserve energy with that item.

Let's Document
Electricity & Natural Gas Conservation

CHALLENGE ACTIVITY -
Learning To Understand Electrical & Natural Gas Home Usage

1) Have each of the children find out how much electricity their families use. This can be done by learning to read the electric meters and locating the number of kilowatt hours consumed.

This information can also be obtained from looking at the kilowatt hours used from your monthly electrical bill.

2) Have the children bring in this information and graph the results.

3) Have the children *(with the help of their parents)* make a good effort the next month to conserve energy.

4) After the month has passed have the children once again bring in the kilowatt hours consumed. Graph those results.

Was there a difference?
How many families were able to conserve energy?

AT SCHOOL

Try this same activity at your school.

How many kilowatt hours does your school use? Make a school project of conserving energy. Send classroom representatives to the other classrooms to encourage them to help your class conserve energy in school. Make posters to display around the school to encourage energy conservation. Check your results the following month. Did your school conserve energy?

(THE SAME ACTIVITIES CAN BE DONE WITH THE GAS METER.)

Practice Reading These Bills

ELECTRIC BILL

```
ELECTRIC RESIDENTIAL METER# -    D021445773

Reading Date 12-11   32 days        1014 KWH
             11-09

Basic Charge                        $4.50
Energy Charge 1000 KWH AT $.05720   $57.50
              14 KWH AT $.05490       .77
Fuel Clause   1014 KWH AT $.00093     .94
Adjustment                          _____
SUBTOTAL                            63.41
   State Tax at 6.0%                  3.80
CURRENT MONTHS BILL                 67.21

Daily Energy Use Comparisons
This Period Last Year               37.0 KWH
This Period This  Year              31.7 KWH
```

GAS BILL

```
                Meter Number: 47739076
Reading on Apr 17 90 (Estimated)     2553
Reading on Mar 16 90 (Estimated)     2415
BTU Multiplier:_____1.004
Gas used in 30 days _____ 139 CCF

Customer charge                    $3.00
   (Includes 3 CCF)
GAS Charge                         65.80
   (136 CCF @ $.48384)
Purchased Gas Adjustment  11.10CR
   (139 CCF @ $.079886 CR)
Total Current Billing _____    $57.70

Average Daily Gas Usage:
This Period This Year:             4.3 CCF
This Period Last Year:             5.7 CCF
```

Conserving Gasoline - Conserves Energy

As you have looked around your community you have probably noticed many different gas stations. In observing all the different gas stations it doesn't seem possible that we could ever run out of gas - **BUT . . .**

back in 1973, the United States found itself in shock when we actually experienced a very limited supply of gasoline for the American people to purchase. Several oil-producing countries suddenly decided to stop selling oil to our country. That meant that gasoline and petroleum-based products were not as readily available as they had been in the past. People were forced to wait for hours in very long lines at the gas stations.

Fossil fuels *(coal, oil, and natural gas)* are made from the buried remains of plants and animals. We cannot simply create more fossil fuels when we feel like it or when we run out. Fossil fuels are created by a natural earth process that takes a great deal of time.

Not only are we unable to make fossil fuels on demand, we also know that burning fossil fuels causes pollution.

So we have two reasons to conserve gasoline:

> ## 1) We do not want to dramatically reduce our supply of fossil fuels, and,
>
> ## 2) We do not want to add pollutants to our earth.

Conserving Gasoline -
Conserves Energy con't

EXPERIMENT
TO BE DONE BY AN ADULT -
CHILDREN ARE TO BE OBSERVERS

The teacher or parent should put a white sock over the exhaust tailpipe of a car. Turn on the car and let it run for just a couple of minutes. Remove the sock - OH MY! WHAT A MESS!

Can you imagine all the pollution that cars are sending up into the air?

In the preceding units we have discussed ways that would help us conserve gasoline. Here is a review and some additional ideas:

• Make shopping lists so you do not have to drive back to the store to purchase a forgotten item.

• Arrange to car-pool whenever possible; girl scouts, music lessons, athletic events, go shopping together with friends, encourage working parents to share rides with their fellow workers.

• Encourage your parents to keep their cars well-tuned. A car that is in good running order will achieve its best possible gas mileage.

• If your parents are looking to purchase a new car, encourage them to look at cars with high gas mileage (usually a smaller car). It is better for the environment and it will save them money.

• Keep the tires of your family car filled with an adequate amount of air. Cars that do not have properly inflated tires will get poor gas mileage.

As much as we know we should try to accomplish the above ideas - we sometimes forget!

Conserving Gasoline -
Conserves Energy con't

HOW MANY PEOPLE ARE SHARING RIDES

Conduct a survey on your street. Sit with a friend (*a very safe distance away from the street*). Count all the cars that go by with only 1 person in the car. Also keep count of all the cars that go by with more than one person in the car.

As a class talk about your findings.

How many cars had only 1 person in the car?

How many cars had more than 1 person in the car?

Graph your findings.

Use the example next to this activity as a way to record your observations.

A CLASS COMMUNITY PROJECT

As a class project, design a community campaign to encourage the public to conserve their use of gasoline.

There are a variety of fun projects that you can incorporate into your campaign. Here are a few suggestions. Be sure to add some of your own ideas to your community awareness campaign.

• Make flyers or posters with gasoline conservation tips. Put up your flyers and posters in your local library and stores. (*Make sure you get permission to put up your flyers from the people in charge of the locations you choose.*)

• Design a Bumper Sticker for your parent's car that encourages gasoline conservation. (*A Bumper Sticker pattern is included on the following page.*)

Gasoline Conservation
Bumper Sticker Pattern

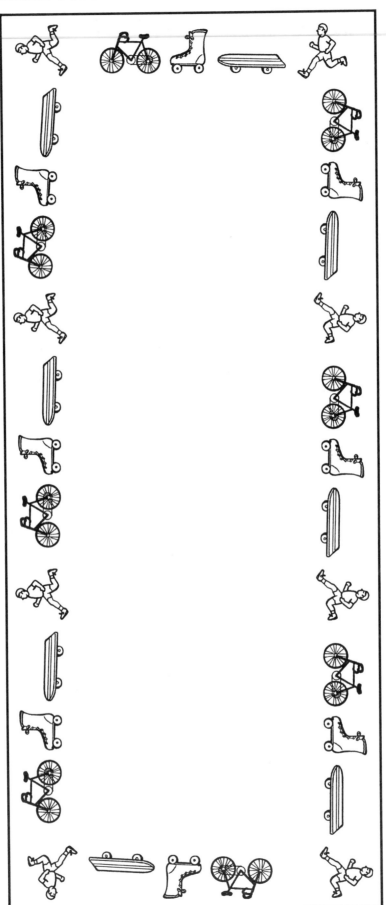

Treat The Earth Gently

Batteries - Batteries - Batteries

A battery is a very small object that gives us energy. Batteries are used in toys, cameras, radios, tape players, calculators, flashlights, just to mention a few things.

A battery may look harmless, but it isn't! A battery can be very harmful to our environment. Batteries are filled with **mercury.** Mercury is a very dangerous and poisonous substance. When a battery is thrown-away in a landfill, the mercury from the battery can leak into the ground and pollute the water.

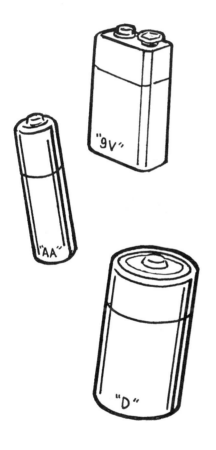

Here are some simple suggestions to ease the battery pollution problem:

• **Purchase rechargable batteries.** A rechargable battery will cost more than a regular battery, but it will quickly pay for itself and will end up saving you money. When a rechargable battery wears out, all you need to do is put it in a *recharger* and it will work again. Rechargable batteries are meant to be **"REUSED."**

• If you have disposable batteries, make sure that you **properly dispose of the battery when it wears out.** A battery containing mercury should be treated as hazardous waste and disposed of at a harzardous waste disposal site. *(See page 67 for more information on hazardous waste disposal).*

• Some companies in your community may be recycling batteries. Find out which companies are recycling and then bring them your old batteries.

HOMEWORK - INVESTIGATE YOUR BATTERY USAGE

Go home and count everything in your house that uses batteries. How much money did those batteries cost? How often do you need to replace them?

Now consider how much money you could save if you didn't need to buy those batteries again. Your parents will be impressed with how much money they could save.

Hot Water Conservation

It seems funny that we can save energy by conserving water, but it's true! The water that comes into your house is cold. This cold water comes from lakes, rivers, and underground wells. But, we turn on the water in the bath or shower, the water in the sink, the water in the dishwasher, and the water in the washing machine, and it can come out **HOT!**

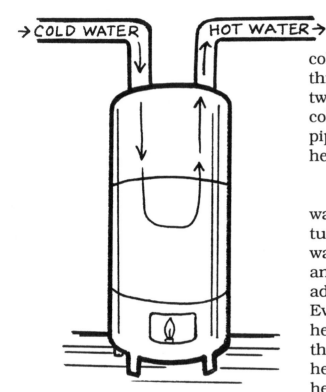

Water is heated in the hot water heater. The cold water that comes into our homes, comes in through a large pipe and then branches off into two pipes. One of the pipes is in charge of the cold water and keeps the water cold. The other pipe directs the cold water to the hot water heater.

The hot water heater fills up with the cold water. When the hot water heater is full it will turn on and heat the water. As we use up the hot water, the hot water heater must fill up again and then heat the water that has just been added. This process goes on all day long. Everytime water is taken out of the hot water heater, the heater must fill up again and heat the new water. In other words, the hot water heater is constantly filling with water and then heating that water. **THIS TAKES A LOT OF ENERGY!**

There are many things that we can do to help this problem:
- We do not have to take cold showers, but it is a good idea to take shorter showers.
- Remember not to leave the hot water running (or any water running)!
- Encourage your parents to only use the dishwasher when it is FULL. Do not use the dishwasher for frequent small loads of dishes. *(Or wash dishes by hand in warm, not hot, water.)*
- Wash large loads of laundry - not frequent small loads. Encourage your parents to wash as much as possible in cold water.
- When you go out of town, turn off the hot water heater.
- Lower the thermostat on the hot water heater to 120° degrees.
- Have your parents wrap the hot water heater in a blanket. You can also insulate the hot water pipes.

Our House Can Actually Conserve Energy!

Almost half of the energy people use in their homes is used in **HEATING** and **COOLING** the house. That is shocking news!

During the **COLD MONTHS** it is so easy to turn up that thermostat to make our home warmer. Everytime we turn up the thermostat we are using more energy. *Consequently, everytime we turn down the thermostat, even just a few degrees, we can save energy. (Never set higher than 68° Fahrenheit.)*

During the **WARM MONTHS**, everytime we lower the thermostat on the air conditioner to make our homes cooler, we are using more energy. *Consequently, everytime we turn up the thermostat, even just a few degrees, (or turn the air conditioner off) we are saving energy. (Never set lower than 72° Fahrenheit.)*

Here are some ideas for regulating the temperature in your homes so you feel comfortable and still save energy.

DURING THE COLD MONTHS

• Dress warmly while you are in your house. Wear socks and a sweater. Don't run around in lightweight clothes and barefeet.

• Have your furnace checked once a year.

• Change the furnace filters frequently. *(Several times a year)* Check the filters monthly.

• Turn down the thermostat 5°. Not only will you save energy, but you will also be sending fewer pollutants into the air, and you will be saving money.

DURING THE WARM MONTHS

• If possible, do not use an air conditioner. If you are uncomfortable try using a fan. Fans do not use as much energy as air conditioning systems.

• Keep your air conditioning system clean. The filters need to be checked regularly and cleaned.

• When you use an air conditioner make sure that the thermostat is set no lower than 72 degrees Fahrenheit.

• Plant shade trees, or add shades around your house to shelter from intense sunlight.

Our House Can Actually Conserve Energy! con't

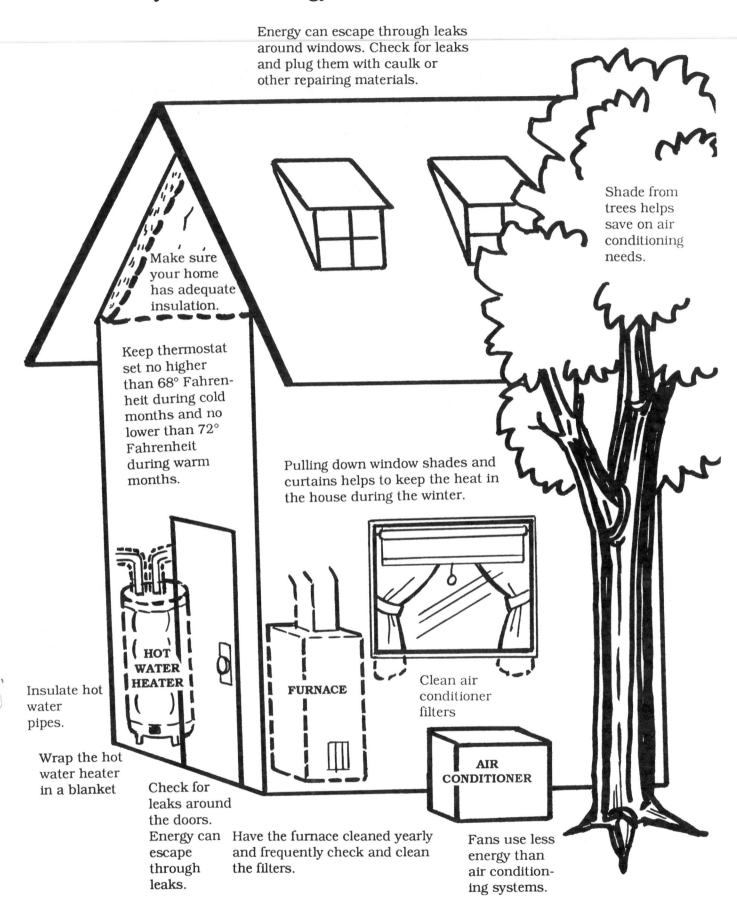

Energy can escape through leaks around windows. Check for leaks and plug them with caulk or other repairing materials.

Shade from trees helps save on air conditioning needs.

Make sure your home has adequate insulation.

Keep thermostat set no higher than 68° Fahrenheit during cold months and no lower than 72° Fahrenheit during warm months.

Pulling down window shades and curtains helps to keep the heat in the house during the winter.

HOT WATER HEATER

FURNACE

Clean air conditioner filters

AIR CONDITIONER

Insulate hot water pipes.

Wrap the hot water heater in a blanket

Check for leaks around the doors. Energy can escape through leaks.

Have the furnace cleaned yearly and frequently check and clean the filters.

Fans use less energy than air conditioning systems.

The Importance of Conservation & Efficiency

Scientists have begun some remarkable work in trying to discover and perfect some alternative energy sources, other than burning fossil fuels or using nuclear energy. While some of the "ideas-of-the-future" sound exciting, we are many years away from having the ability to make these energy sources commonplace.

Before you read on any farther about the alternative energy sources, it is very important that we stop here for a moment to remember that:

> **The key to saving our environment _right now_ is through;**
>
> **CONSERVATION** - which means not using as much energy and being careful with the energy sources that we already have,
>
> AND . . .
>
> **EFFICIENCY** - which means making sure that we are not wasting our energy resources.

We must use our current energy resources with a great deal of wisdom. We cannot rely on the discoveries of the future to solve today's problems. The new energy alternatives that you will be reading about will never take the place of **CONSERVATION** and **EFFICIENCY.**

Color these awards and wear them proudly!

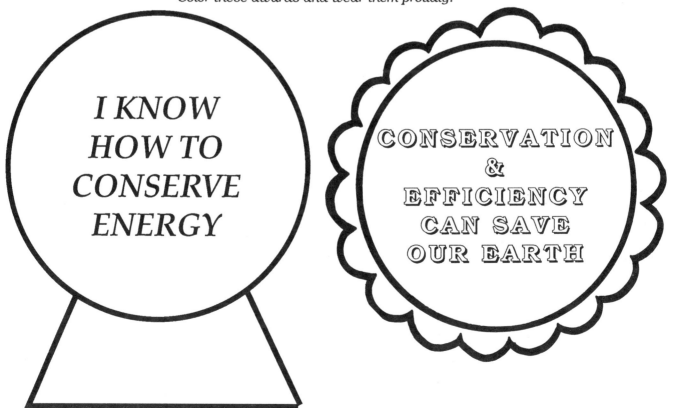

An Energy Alternative - WIND

People have known for hundreds of years that **WIND** can provide us with a powerful energy source. Windmills have been used to pump water and the wind has been used for moving sailing ships across the ocean.

Today on some farms in the United States, windmills are being used to pump water from deep wells for irrigation *(to supply farm land with water)*. Wind is also being used to power turbines *(machines)* which generate electricity. It is estimated that the United States has enough wind energy to provide a quarter of our nation with electricity. In some parts of the United States we are already creating electricity using wind energy. Fifteen percent of San Francisco's electricity is created from wind energy.

Right now there are approximately 95 countries that are using the wind as an energy source.

This sounds so simple! It sounds so easy! Why don't we have more wind energy available right now! Here are some answers:

• Wind energy costs a lot of money. Throughout the past few years the amount of money that has been put into developing wind energy has decreased.

• Just like when you read about people saying that they "don't want a landfill in their neighborhood," some people have said, "we don't want wind energy in our neighborhood." Wind energy can be very noisy.

EXPERIMENT - FEEL THE ENERGY OF THE WIND

Needed: Small mouth jar, one-hole cork to fit in jar snugly, clear straw of glass tubing, water, food coloring, paraffin or plasticene.

What You Do: Fill the bottle about 1/2 full with colored water. Insert the tubing (straw) through the one-hole cork so that it extends about 1/2 inch from the bottom of the bottle. Put the cork and tubing in the mouth of the bottle and seal with plasticene (children) or paraffin (teacher). The apparatus should be checked to see if it is air-tight. Blow into the straw as hard as you can causing bubbling in the water. What happens when the blowing stops?

TEACHER TIP: A rubber stopper tends to seal the bottle more efficiently than cork. If you use glass tubing, it will be easier to insert in the stopper if both are wet. Children should never handle glass tubing.

Make Your Own Windmill

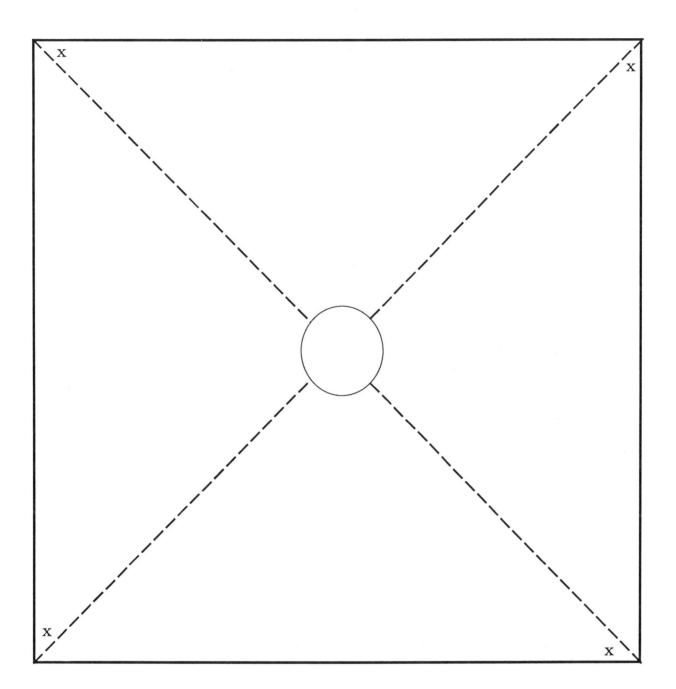

Directions:
Cut out the square. Cut on the dotted-lines. Fold the corners marked "x" to the center circle, overlap and insert a fastner.

  Treat The Earth Gently

An Energy Alternative - SOLAR

SOLAR ENERGY means energy from the sun.

Solar energy is an energy source that people have known about for hundreds of years. The first solar water heater was sold in the United States 200 years ago, and is still being sold today.

Solar energy is one of the simplest energy producing systems available. Unfortunately it is still very expensive. A solar water heater for a home can cost up to $4,000, whereby a natural gas water heater can cost as little as $200. Although one's monthly gas bills would decrease, the initial expense is still too large for many people to be able to afford.

Solar power can also be used to heat our homes. Large solar panels *(solar collectors)* are installed on the roofs of homes. The heat from the sun is collected in the panels and the home is heated from the sun. The country of Israel is probably the world leader in heating homes with solar energy. Look around your community and you may see solar collectors on the rooftops of houses or apartment buildings. Have you seen any?

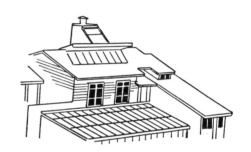

Cars are another object that can be powered by solar energy. The solar powered cars use energy from sunlight. Solar cells are mounted on the cars. It is the solar cells that turn the solar energy into electricity. Once again, solar cars are expensive to manufacture.

One item that is solar powered that most all of us have had an opportunity to use is a solar powered calculator.

EXPERIMENT
Does The Sun Still Shine On A Cloudy Day?

Needed: Heavy wax paper; flashlight, cotton batting.

What You Do: After observing clouds outside, the children can cut a "cloud" shape from wax paper. In a darkened room, they can hold their clouds in front of the flashlight. What happens to the light of the "sun?" Is the sun still shining? What happens when we make the clouds thicker? Repeat the experiment using cotton batting. What makes us think the sun is not shining on a cloudy day?

An Energy Alternative - HYDRO

HYDRO-POWER means energy that comes from water.

If you have ever seen a waterfall or stood in a rushing stream, it is easy to see and feel the energy created by the force of water.

Hydropower creates about 25 percent of the world's electricity! That's impressive! The best news about hydropower is that it does not send any greenhouse-producing gases into the air.

Although hydropower sounds like another great energy alternative it is not without complications. The United States and the rest of the world have thousands of dams already in place, but most of them are not being used for creating energy. Unfortunately many of the dams we have built are gigantic. The United States has 18 dams over 490 feet tall.

When dams this size are built, forests and wildlife habitats are destroyed, flooding, and possible water pollution occurs. Not only are there environmental concerns with the actual building of large dams, but they are also expensive and we have only limited experience in operating large hydropower systems.

In the future we will probably be seeing "micro-hydro" generators. This means we will see very small hydropower plants. These plants may require dams that are only several feet tall. In creating small hydropower plants and smaller dams, destruction of the forests woud decrease, less wildlife would be in danger and pollution could be decreased.

--- **EXPERIMENT - Can Water Move Things?** ---

Needed: Sink with a faucet and a plastic pinwheel.

What You Do: This experiment will help the children see how water can create power and move things. Hold the pinwheel under the faucet in the line of the direction of water flow. Turn on the water. What happens to the pinwheel?

An Energy Alternative - GEOTHERMAL

GEOTHERMAL ENERGY
means harnessing the earth's heat from below the surface.
This heat is created by underground hot water springs
and steam geysers.

There are approximately 150 geothermal-powered electric plants in the world. These plants are primarily located along the Pacific Rim and coastlines of New Zealand, New Guinea, Western Siberia, the United States, Mexico, and Central and South America.

Color the Pacific Rim and coastline areas of the above mentioned countries and continents.

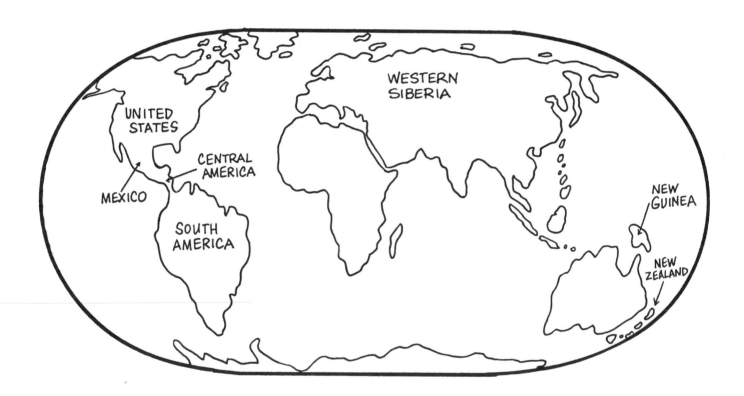

In order to effectively use geothermal energy you have to live near a coastline where this form of energy can be found. At this point in time it is not possible to transport geothermal energy.

We have just begun to explore the geothermal energy source. It's total potential will probably not be understood for years. But until that time, researchers and scientists are continuing their study of geothermal energy.

AN ENERGY CONSERVATION HUNT

Take a walk through each room in your house. Write down all the ways that you could save energy in that room. Share your findings with the rest of the class.

BEDROOM

LIVING ROOM

BATHROOM

KITCHEN

BASEMENT

FURNANCE ROOM

Treat The Earth Gently

Draw a picture of an object-of-the-future that uses each of the following forms of alternative energy.

WIND ENERGY	**SOLAR ENERGY**
HYDRO ENERGY	**GEOTHERMAL ENERGY**

Unit 6

ENDANGERED ANIMALS

CONTENTS

Why Study The Problems Of Animals?

Giant Panda

The study of animals, at first glance, may not seem to make sense when you are studying the environmental problems of the earth. However, as you take a closer look you will understand why we need to study and help protect all the animals of the earth.

Black Rhino

1) All living creatures are important to the earth. Every animal has an important part in the chain of nature. If one kind of animal disappears forever it will cause some type of change on our planet.

2) Many animals are in trouble because people are ruining the land *(habitat)* where the animals live. We need to learn how to protect the earth for the animals as well as for people.

In this unit we are going to look at **WHY** so many animals are on the Endangered Species List, and we will learn more about some very interesting animals who are in danger!

DEFINITIONS - What Is An Endangered Animal?

Before we begin our study of endangered animals you should understand what an endangered animal is. Is it an animal that is dangerous? Of course not! An endangered animal is one that is in immediate danger of dying *(becoming extinct)* if protective measures are not taken. **BIOLOGISTS** *(scientists that study living things)* have identified one and one-half million species that are in danger of becoming extinct.

EXTINCT SPECIES - A type of animal that is no longer living. Not even one can be found on the earth.

ENDANGERED SPECIES - Animals that are in immediate danger of becoming extinct.

THREATENED SPECIES - Animals that could very soon become endangered because their numbers are rapidly decreasing.

EXTINCTION - Is It Natural Or Not?

EXTINCTION is a natural process. For millions of years different types of animals and plants have lived and then become extinct. We don't always know why a species has become extinct, but we do know that extinction can be caused by natural occurrences. Sometimes natural disasters such as floods, volcanoes and natural changes in the climate can cause a species to become extinct. Sometimes extinction is caused by a combination of causes, such as a climate change and a lack of food or competition for food.

Millions of years ago dinosaurs walked the earth. It would have been so much fun to have been able to watch them! Dinosaurs died-out because of mass-extinction. **MASS-EXTINCTION** is when a large group of animals die off at about the same time. Some scientists believe that the climate and temperature of the earth changed so quickly that it caused all the dinosaurs to die. Other scientists believe that a series of natural diasters, over many years, caused the extinction of the dinosaurs. For our purposes it really doesn't matter which group of scientists are correct. What is important is that we realize that dinosaurs became extinct because of some natural process.

CAN YOU NAME AND MAKE SOME OF THE DINOSAURS?

As a class project, make a list of as many of the dinosaurs as you can. After you have completed your list, go to the library and look up these dinosaurs in various reference books.

Assign one dinosaur to each student in the class. Have each of the children make their assigned dinosaur out of modeling clay. Display the clay dinosaurs on a table.

Beside each dinosaur have the children write some information about that dinosaur on a 3" x 5" index card. Fold the card in two so that it can stand up by the dinosaur.

Are People Causing
The Extinction Of Animals?

**Today we are worried about extinction because the extinction
process that we are seeing is not natural.
It is being caused by people!**

The last **DODO BIRD** was seen in 1681. The story of the dodo is a sad one. Hundreds of years ago dodos lived on the island of Mauritius in the Indian Ocean. Dodos were large birds who couldn't fly or run very fast. European sailors came to the island of Mauritius and discovered that dodo birds were easy to catch and tasted pretty good. Not only were the dodos hunted for food, but the dodos also died because the sailors brought pigs, dogs, and cats to the island. The pigs, dogs, and cats ate the dodo bird eggs and baby dodos. It didn't take many years until there were not any dodo birds left! People caused the extinction of the dodo bird.

Dodo Bird

Passenger Pigeon

In 1914, the last **PASSENGER PIGEON** died in the Cincinnati Zoo. While the dodo birds died because of hunting, the passenger pigeons died because they lost their homes. People cut down the forests where the passenger pigeons lived. The birds were losing their homes faster than they were able to reproduce in number. Animals depend on the environment for their survival. When people destroy where animals live, the animals will die too!

When an animal becomes extinct because of a natural process, it simply means that the earth has changed and more than likely another new species of animal will emerge. We may not have dinosaurs anymore, but we do have elephants and whales. It is always sad when a species dies, but we can accept that loss when it occurs naturally. The extinction and near extinction of animals today is not natural. People are causing this because we are not caring for our environment.

FIND OUT MORE
ABOUT AN EXTINCT ANIMAL!

Many of you had probably never heard of the dodo bird or the passenger pigeon. Unfortunately, there are many animals that are now extinct. Research an extinct animal. Write a short report and share what you have learned with the class. Draw a picture of the animal.

Hunting and Collecting

In the next three lessons we are going to take a look at some of the reasons why so many animals are ending up on the Endangered Species List.

Two of the reasons are **HUNTING** and **COLLECTING.** While it is illegal in most countries to kill or collect an endangered animal it is still happening.

ENDANGERED ANIMALS AS PETS - OH NO!

Lears Macaw

MACAWS are large, brightly colored parrots. Over the years many of these birds have been taken from the wild and have been sold as pets. Unfortunately, people quickly learn that large parrots are difficult to keep in captivity. These parrots can be very noisy and messy. Most people are unable to keep them. Not only is it illegal to have an endangered animal as a pet, but we need to remember that these animals belong in their natural habitat. Currently, there are fewer than 100 Lears Macaws in existence.

HUNTING - ANIMAL PRODUCTS

So many beautiful and interesting animals are killed each year so that people can use parts of the animals to make various products. It is shocking to discover how many things people make from animals.

FUR - Fur coats, articles of clothing with fur trim, rugs and wall hangings are still being sold worldwide. While it is illegal in most countries to kill an endangered animal or sell products made from an endangered animal it is still happening.

TIGERS have been the victims of illegal hunting, because their beautiful fur is wanted to make coats, rugs, and wall hangings. People will spend $2,000 for one tiger skin. There are only 4,000 tigers remaining in the wilds of India.

SNOW LEOPARDS, JAGUARS, CHEETAHS and **CLOUDED LEOPARDS** are all endangered large cats that are still being hunted and killed for their beautiful fur.

Tiger

Hunting and Collecting

IVORY - The **AFRICAN ELE-PHANT,** the world' largest land animal, is a member of a treatened population. The African Elephant has been killed for it's ivory tusks. People use the ivory to make jewelry and various carvings and sculptures. In 1989, the United States banned the importing of ivory. It is still estimated that 90% of the ivory sold is done illegally.

In 1979 there were 1,300,000 African Elephants. Today there are less than 650,000. Each year 90,000 adult elephants are killed for their ivory. Another 10,000 young elephants die as a result of losing the adult elephants who cared for them.

African Elephant

HORNS - BLACK RHINOS are an endangered species that are killed for their horns. In some Asian countries the Rhino horns are ground into medicine. Rhino horns have also been used for making handles of daggers. There are less than 5,000 Black Rhinos alive today.

Black Rhino

CROCODILES, although not the most attractive animal, have been killed for it's **SKIN.** Crocodile skin has been used to make shoes, belts, purses, suitcases, just to name a few products. Almost every type of crocodile is found on the Endangered Species List.

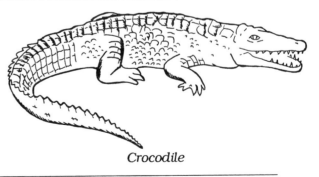

Crocodile

Hunting and Collecting

The **HUMPBACK WHALE** is another huge animal who has suffered an amazing reduction in population due to hunting. At one time there were over 100,000 Humpback Whales. By the mid-60s the population had fallen to about 6,000. The whales were hunted for their **WHALE OIL.** Whale oil is burned in lamps and can be made into **SOAP** and **WAX. WHALE MEAT** can also be eaten. In the mid-1980s most countries had stopped "whaling." There are many other types of whales on the Endangered Species List.

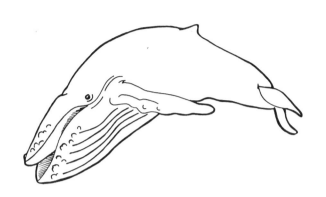

Humpback Whale

——— HUNTING OUT OF FEAR ———

Many animals have been killed because people are afraid of them or view them as "pests."

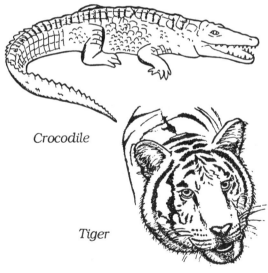

TIGERS have been killed because many people think of them as "man-eating." While it is true that tigers are a powerful and dangerous animal, most tigers do not seek out and attack people. Scientists feel that tigers who hunt people are either injured or very old so they are unable to hunt their normal prey. **CROCODILES** are another animal that is killed because people have attached a "man-eating" tag on them.

Crocodile

Tiger

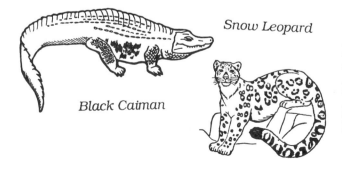

Snow Leopard

Black Caiman

The **SNOW LEOPARD** and the **BLACK CAIMAN** are two animals on the Endangered Species List that have been hunted and killed because people believed they were a threat to livestock.

CARELESSLY KILLED!

DOLPHINS have been the victims of the tuna fishing industry for years. In 1987, 115,000 dolphins were drowned when they were caught in tuna fishing nets. These nets are called seines. For some reason, groups of tuna enjoy swimming below dolphins. Dolphins swim near the top of the water so they are easy for the fishing boats to spot. Thanks to people boycotting the tuna industry, several of the world's largest tuna companies are finding alternative ways to catch tuna. Look for the "DOLPHIN-SAFE" labels on the tuna cans in your store and don't buy any tuna fish can without this label.

Thousands of **SEA TURTLES** have been caught and drowned in the nets of shrimp fishing boats. Shrimp fisherman are supposed to use a *Turtle Excluder Device* (TED) so that the Sea Turtles are not caught. Unfortunately, not all shrimp fisherman are using the TED device.

Sea Turtles are also being killed by consuming pollution that they find in the water, such as plastic bags and balloons. Sea Turtles mistake the plastic and balloons for one of their favorite foods, jellyfish. Sea Turtles are also caught for food (turtle soup) and for making products from their shells.

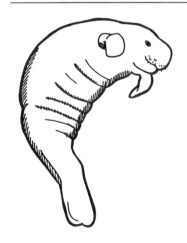

MANATEES are huge, peaceful, slow-moving animals that live in the water near the state of Florida. The worst enemy of the Manatee are motorboats. Since manatees are very slow-moving they cannot get out of the way of the boats fast enough and because they are unafraid of people they often swim near boaters.They swim right below the surface of the water so boaters frequently do not see the manatees until it is too late.

Sea Cow is the nick-name for the Manatee.

Name _____

Write something that you have learned about each of the animals. Draw a picture on the back of the paper of your favorite animal.

Lear's Macaw _____

_____

Indian Tiger _____

_____

African Elephant _____

_____

Black Rhino _____

_____

Humpback Whale _____

_____

Crocodile _____

_____

Dolphin _____

_____

Sea Turtle _____

_____

Manatee _____

_____

Habitat and Population

HABITAT is another name for the place where animals and plants live naturally. The loss of habitat is the leading reason why so many animals are in danger of becoming extinct. This means that many, many animals are losing their homes. Just like the Passenger Pigeon that you learned about on page 95, they are now extinct because they lost the forests where they lived.

Giant Panda

Many animals need a very specific type of habitat for their survival. **GIANT PANDAS** must have bamboo forests to live in. Without an adequate supply of bamboo, pandas will starve.

Most animals need to live in the type of habitat that best suits their survival needs. When habitats are destroyed, the **animals do not have a place to live, they are not able to find adequate food sources, and they are unable to raise their young.**

Animals are not destroying their habitats - people are! Why? There are many reasons. Here are a few of the major causes:

GROWING POPULATION

There are more and more and more people! With more people comes more construction. We build cities and roads and highways. We clear the land and forests to grow more crops. We are not only cutting down the forests, but we are also filling in the swampland to build on top of. Loss of swampland is one of the reasons why crocodiles are now on the Endangered SpeciesList.

DOMESTIC ANIMALS

Cows, sheep, goats, and horses are animals that we call domestic animals. Animals who work for people. To care for these animals much land and natural habitats have been destroyed. Thousands of acres in the Central and South American rain forests have been lost to grazing land for the domestic animals. The **GIANT SOUTH AMERICAN OTTER**, many **BIRDS** and **MONKEYS** are now on the Endangered Species List because they have lost their homes and their natural food sources are dimished or eliminated.

PEOPLE PRODUCTS

So many products that we use come from the natural habitats of animals. We cut down millions of trees for the lumber used in construction. We have drilled deep into the earth for coal, oil, gold, and many other materials that people buy.

Give each child one of the following animals. Ask the children to do some research about their animal. The children should write one paragraph explaining how the loss of habitat has affected their animal. Make a copy of the animal names and let the children each draw a name out of a hat.

White Rhino	**Brown Hyena**
Wallaby	**Numbat**
Cheetah	**Clouded Leopard**
Bison	**African Elephant**
Tiger	**Komodo Dragon**
Golden Lion Tamarin	**African Hunting Dogs**
Muriqui	**Giant Panda**
Black Rhino	**Giant Otter**
Lemurs	**Scarlet Macaw**
Wombat	**Urial**
Mountain Gorilla	**Jaguar**
Crocodile	**Wild Yak**
Snow Leopard	**Flying Foxes**

RESEARCHING & REPORTING ABOUT AN ENDANGERED ANIMAL

(Worksheet to assist in recording information)

Name of Animal: _____

Natural Habitat: *(i.e, water, forest, etc.)* _____
_____

Animal is found in these countries: _____
_____
_____

Natural prey or food source for the animal: _____
_____
_____

Natural enemies of the animal: _____
_____
_____

How old can the animal live to be? _____
_____
_____

Some of the reasons why this animal is on the Endangered Species List:
_____
_____
_____
_____
_____
_____
_____
_____
_____
_____
_____

CLASS PROJECTS

WHAT TO BUY or WHAT NOT TO BUY? - That is the question!

As a class, make a list of all the products that you can think of that could be made from endangered animals. Look through catalogs to help you get some ideas. What could you purchase instead of these items?

A TROPICAL RAIN FOREST

Begin this project by explaining to the children how thick, dense, and moist a tropical rain forest is. Talk about the climate. How much sunlight reaches into a tropical rain forest? How much moisture is there?

Here is a visual experience for the children that will help the children to actually see how destroying forests endangers animals.

1) Fill a 9" x 13" cake pan with soil. Plant grass seeds. Wait to continue your observations until the grass has grown thick.

2) Once the grass has grown, fill the pan with small plastic or construction paper animals. You might wish to use monkeys, parrots, and a variety of other animals that are actually found in a rain forest. Have the children look at all the animals that are in the forest. What a wonderful place for them to live!

3) Over the next several days, dig out part of the rain forest. Those animals that were living in the part of the rain forest that was destroyed can be removed from the pan. You might also wish to remove some of the animals and move others into the remaining parts of the rain forest. Discuss food sources. Do you think that there are adequate food sources for the overcrowded sections of the rain forest?

4) Continue the process of removing the grass and some of the animals until there isn't any rain forest left in your pan. The children will also see that there are no longer any animals either.

Pollutions & Poisons

It is very sad to think that pollutants, poisons, and pesticides that people have created are now killing animals.

In the acid rain unit you learned about how acid rain, which is caused by pollution, is seriously damaging our forests, the water, and is harming the animals. There are other environmental problems, besides acid rain, which are threatening the animals.

Right here in the United States scientists discovered that the **PEREGRINE FALCONS** were nearly extinct. Peregrine Falcons suffered dramatic loses because of a pesticide called **DDT.** DDT was used for killing insects that were damaging crops. The interesting discovery about the loss of Peregrine Falcons and the use of DDT was that the Peregrine Falcons were *not eating* the plants that contained the DDT, and they were *not eating* the insects which contained DDT.

Peregrine Falcons feed on other smaller birds. The birds that the Peregrine Falcons were eating were the birds who had eaten the insects from the DDT infested crops. The DDT built up in the Peregrine Falcons, but did not cause them to die. The DDT killed the Peregrine Falcon babies. The DDT caused the Peregrine Falcons to lay eggs that had very soft shells. Most of the baby Peregrine Falcons were crushed to death while still in the egg by the parent birds sitting on them to keep the eggs warm. Egg shells need to be hard to maintain the weight of the parent bird. The DDT had destroyed the Peregrine Falcons ability to lay eggs with strong shells. Before long there were not many Peregrine Falcons left. They were nearly extinct.

A HAPPIER ENDING . . .

Peregrine Falcons are being raised in captivity in the United States and Canada. Scientists are very carefully treating the birds just like their parents. These birds are then released back into the wild. The program has been very successful.

Pollution In The Water

Besides hunting and careless killings, *animals of the water* have many other problems that threaten their existence.

OIL SPILLS IN THE WATER

What happens to the animal life when there is an oil spill? The oil clogs the gills of **FISH.** Fish need their gills to breathe. If their gills are clogged, fish are unable to live.

SEA OTTERS have beautiful coats of fur that protect them from cold temperatures in the water. The oil from an oil spill coats the otter's fur so that they are no longer safely protected.

Oil spills also affect the lives of **MAMMALS** and **BIRDS** who need the water for survival.

PLASTIC POLLUTION IN THE WATER

We throw away so many plastic materials into the water. Everything from helium balloons that floated away and then landed in the water, to plastic bags, and small plastic objects. Many **FISH** and other aquatic life mistake the plastic objects for food. The animals consume the plastic and because it cannot be digested it often will kill the animal. Other animals become caught and trapped in plastic and plastic nets. Plastic wrap, bags, and rings can also get caught around the beaks of birds. **SEA TURTLES** have mistakenly eaten plastic materials. It is believed that this is causing the death of many animals.

Clip Art Animals

Enlarge the animal patterns and use on posters or as puppets for a creative dramatics presentation. The pictures can also be used in reports on endangered animals.

SHARING WHAT YOU'VE LEARNED WITH OTHERS

Pages 110 - 111

ORGANIZATIONS TO CONTACT

Page 112

Sharing What You've Learned With Others

When you have finished the book, *Treat The Earth Gently*, you will have become a very well-informed person. Now it is time to put your knowledge into action!

There are many things that children can do to help inform other people about our environmental concerns, and ways that we can help the environment. In each of the units you were given ideas about some specific ways you can help our earth.

- Remember not to purchase CFC containing products.
- Be careful about what products you purchase that may have been made from an endangered animal.
- Conserve energy at home and at school.
- Be watchful of hazardous waste containing products.
- Reduce - Reuse - Recycle

Just to remind you of a few examples!

But - one of the best ways to help clean up and repair our environment is to share what you have learned with others! Encourage other people to learn more! Here are some ideas:

TEACH PEOPLE

Tell your parents, friends, and neighbors. After your study of the environment you could very possibly know more about the earth's problems and solutions than the adults around you! Teach them!

A SCHOOL ENVIRONMENTAL NEWSPAPER

Start a school environmental newspaper. Write articles about environmental problems. Provide "tips" in your newspaper that will help conserve energy, or help people learn how to become better "Reuser's - Reducer's - and Recyclers!"

A SCHOOL-BASED RECYCLING PROGRAM

If your school is not already recycling begin a recycling program. Teach everyone how to sort waste and how to dispose of it properly. Call your neighborhood or community recycling program to get tips about how to start.

Write Government Officials

The government needs to hear from kids just like you! Our nation's leaders and the leaders of other countries need to hear our concerns. Most government officials welcome letters and want to know your thoughts.

Write letters that clearly state what you are concerned about and why you are concerned. Using the information that you have learned will help influence the people who make decisions about the laws and funding that govern the safety of our planet.

> **NO MATTER HOW YOUNG YOU ARE -**
> **YOU CAN MAKE A DIFFERENCE.**

Here are some addresses of where to write to our government officials and to the governments of Japan and Russia.

Representative _____   Senator _____
US House of Representatives   US Sentate
Washington DC 20515   Washington DC 20510

(You will need to know the names of your state's Senators and Representatives.)

President George Bush
The White House
1600 Pennsylvania Ave
Washington DC 20500
(Begin your letter, "Dear Mr. President.")

The
Russian
Leader

General Secretary Mikhail Sergeyevich Gorbachev
Secretariat of the CPSU,
Central Committee,
Staraya Ploshchad 4
Moscow, 103132, The U.S.S.R.

The
Japanese
Leader

Prime Minister Toshiki Kaifu
Nagata-Cho,
Chiyoda-Ku
Tokyo, 100, Japan

If you wish to write to the leaders of other foreign countries, request the proper address from:

<u>(Country's Name)</u> Embassy
The United Nations,
United Nations Plaza
New York, NY 10017

Organizations To Contact

The Acid Rain Foundation
1630 Blackhawk Hills
St. Paul, MN 55122

Acid Rain Information
    Clearinghouse Library
Center For Environmental
    Information, Inc.
33 S. Washington St.
Rochester, NY 14608

Adopt-A-Stream Foundation
P.O. Box 5558
Everett, WA 98201

Air Pollution Control
Bureau of National Affairs Inc.
1231 25th St. NW
Washington DC 20037

Alliance To Save ENergy
1925 K St. NW - Suite 206
Washington DC 20036

American Association of Zoological
    Parks and Aquariums
Oglebay Park
Wheeling, WV 26003

American Wind Energy Association
1730 N Lynn St. - Suite 610
Arlington, VA 22209

Canadian Coalition On Acid Rain
112 St. Clair Ave West - Suite 504
Toronto, Ontario, Canada M4V 2Y3

Center for Marine Conservation
1725 DeSales St NW - Suite 500
Washington DC 20036

Friends of The Earth
530 Seventh St SE
Washington DC 20003

Global Releaf, c/o the American
    Forestry Association
P.O. Box 2000
Washington DC 20013

Greenpeace
1436 U Street NW
Washington DC 20009

Household Hazardous Waste Project
901 S. National Ave - Box 108
Springfield, MO 65804

National Association of Recycling
    Industries
330 Madison Ave
New York, NY 10017

National Clean Air Coalition
530 7th St SE
Washington DC 20003

National Wildlife Federation
1412 16th St. NW
Washington DC 20036

Public Affairs Office
US Environmental Protection Agency
Washington DC 20036

Renew America
1400 16th St. NW - Suite 710
Washington DC 20036

Save the Manatee Club
500 N Maitland Ave - Suite 200
Maitland, FL 32751

U.S. Environmental Protection Agency
401 M St. SW
Washington DC 20460

United Nations Environment Programme
North American Office
Room DC2-0803, United Nations
New York, NY 10017

The Whale Center
3929 Piedmont Ave
Oakland, CA 94611

Wildlife Conservation International
New York Zoological Society
Bronx, NY 10460

World Society for the Protection of
    Animals
29 Perkins St. P.O. Box 190
Boston, MA 02130

World Wildlife Fund
1250 24th St. NW
Washington DC 20037